A History of Biology

A History of Biology

MAURICE CAULLERY

Honorary Professor at the Sorbonne; Member of the Institute

A SUN BOOK

Translated from the French by James Walling

 Walker and Company · New York

CONTENTS

PREFACE

In this book an attempt has been made to show how we have arrived at our present state of knowledge about the phenomena of life. Reference will be made both to established facts and to other notions that remain veiled in uncertainty and obscurity.

This history of the progress of biology goes back to the earliest ages of humanity. Primitive man had to be something of a biologist in order to defend himself against nature and to survive. It was a vital necessity for him to observe the creatures among which he lived. Considerations of security and food supply led to hunting, to fishing, to gathering wild fruit and eventually to crop growing and stock raising. All these activities provided biological knowledge founded on observation and very soon on experimentation. Thus early man found himself faced with the most fundamental prob-

lems: the essential difference between the living creature and inert matter, the origin of life itself, and the
riddle of death. Our distant ancestors have left traces
of all these preoccupations in the form of cave paint-
ings, rock engravings, statuettes and carvings in bone
and ivory. These provide convincing evidence of their
powers of observation.

Man was soon using animal and vegetable substances for therapeutic ends or as poisons. Such use
may well have been rule of thumb, but it was nevertheless based on experimental tests. Even today some
primitive peoples who have been untouched by civilization have a similar empirical basis to their medical
lore, and individual cases show us that the practical
accuracy of their knowledge is by no means negligible.

The therapeutic properties of cinchona (or quin-
quina) were understood and used by the Indians of
Peru before the seventeenth century, when this knowledge reached Europe, and long before the nineteenth-
century researches of Pelletier and Caventou on the
extraction of alkaloids, one of which is quinine. Curare,
which has been of such value to physiologists, is a
poison used on arrowheads by the Indian tribes
dwelling in the Central Amazon basin. This substance
is prepared with such precision that it is in great
demand in our laboratories. Even in our modern civi-
lized societies, until a very few generations ago, country
people had built up and handed down an abundant
store of accurate empirical biology, based on their
experience of plant growing and stock raising.

Today's scientific biology has gradually emerged from this popular fund of knowledge and has drawn upon every society and every period of man's history.

The gradual building of the amazingly complex structure of modern biology makes a wonderful story of adventure and endeavor. It begins many centuries ago and through numerous vicissitudes brings us to the present day. It is a tale of the contributions made by precise observation, and of the more dubious role of philosophical speculation and intuition; its climax is reached in the strictly controlled experiments of our own day. In this book we have space only for the broad outlines of the story. It is hoped that the reader will be encouraged by this summary to seek more detailed knowledge.

We have, therefore, systematically eliminated all detailed analysis, limiting ourselves strictly to the major developments and their repercussions. But care has been taken not to divorce the discoveries themselves from the personality of the scientists who have contributed most in making those discoveries. It may be true that once a science is evolved it becomes independent of those who built it; it is only just, however, that these good artisans should not be forgotten, and mention of them as individuals will provide the reader with useful points of reference in his assimilation of the collective efforts of succeeding generations of scientists. Moreover, it is important to realize that each of these generations is a prisoner of its own time; even the most enlightened and original minds can never completely cast off the shackles that their period imposes. Thus each discovery is better assessed when viewed in its contemporary setting, and this treatment will, it is hoped, make livelier reading than a mere logical sequence of events. The history of biology is inseparable from those who have made it.

M.C.

A History of Biology

1 / GREEK SCIENCE AND BIOLOGY

To consider only the Mediterranean cradle of our civilization, we must begin with the Egyptians, who founded the science of geometry and were skilled observers and students of nature. This is borne out by their sculpture and the decoration of their tombs (especially those of the Early Empire at Sakkara, 3000—2500 B.C.). Herodotus, who visited Egypt about 500 B.C., recorded in his histories a number of zoological observations made on Egyptian wild life, and Geoffroy Saint-Hilaire was able to confirm the accuracy of these remarks during Napoleon's expedition to the Nile.

But the direct origins of modern biology must be sought in ancient Greece. Greek philosophers, as well as doctors, established a framework of theories and principles out of the mass of practical knowledge handed down by their ancestors. This framework constitutes a real science of considerable proportions.

Three great names stand out: Hippocrates, Aristotle and Galen.

Hippocrates

Greek medicine as practiced by the corporation of the Asclepiads was a highly developed science; indeed, the temples of Aesculapius were veritable hospitals. Hippocrates of Cos (460—380 B.C.) synthesized all the knowledge acquired by his predecessors into something approaching a medical encyclopedia. Not only has this work survived, but it exercised a powerful influence upon modern thought until the seventeenth century and even beyond. Hippocrates' wise intuition in practice filled many of the gaps in his positive knowledge. He conceived good health as a state of balance between the humors, and disease as a disturbance of this harmony. His work covers the whole field of physiology, and in spite of its shortcomings, it is tantamount to a kind of biology. He likewise evolved a system of therapeutics from which botany was to derive. In ancient Greece, as in all other periods of history, the medical profession was well to the fore in pioneering biology.

Aristotle

Aristotle (384—322 B.C.), whose name dominates the whole field of natural sciences in antiquity, belonged to a family of Asclepiads. He synthesized and coordinated the speculative knowledge that he acquired as a pupil of Plato and the positive notions that he gained by his own observations. His work, only part of which has survived, is a condensation of all the knowledge of his predecessors, which he reviewed in the light of personal experience. His various treatises cover a good many branches of biology: anatomy (*On the Parts of Animals, History of Animals,*[1] *Anatomical Descriptions* [non-extant]); embryogeny (*On the Reproduction of Animals*); botany (*History of Plants*, which is also non-extant but is known to us through his pupil Theophrastus, 370—263 B.C.). Aristotle's work, especially in zoology, comprises a considerable fund of positive data many of which have only been re-established in recent centuries. His ideas about anatomy and, above all, physiology are far removed from our modern conceptions; he does not seem to have solid ground for them. But this was inevitable at a time when physics and chemistry were not yet properly constituted sciences. Aristotle did not hesitate to use hypotheses and speculation in support of logic and basic principles. Such was his influence that it continued to weigh heavily on modern thought until the late eighteenth century. He imagined life as an immaterial principle that animates matter and nature as ordained by a supreme intelligence with a purpose in mind;

---

[1]There is an admirable translation into English of the *History of Animals* by Sir D'Arcy W. Thompson, who was both an eminent zoologist and an outstanding Hellenist *(The Works of Aristotle,* Vol. IV; Oxford: Clarendon Press, 1910).

whence the doctrine of the prime importance of final causes. Animism and finalism are the foundations of his biological conceptions, and the most modern history of biology could almost be summarized as the gradual elimination of these two fundamental conceptions. Although they may have been discarded from positive science today they still have supporters in scientific philosophy.

The superior intellects of ancient Greece were by no means inferior to the men of genius of our time. They possessed only a limited number of facts about the concrete universe, and these facts were perceived only superficially. But these limitations opened the way more easily to the conception of vast syntheses in which intuition played the leading role. Intuition may have suggested to them some solutions that seem fanciful today, but others correspond in their general texture to conclusions we have reached on a more solid basis. The founders of ancient science were, in fact, all philosophers who based their arguments on general systems of varying tendencies. Some were imbued with a large dose of mysticism, while others, like Democritus and Epicurus, are almost modern in their positive outlook. The latter succeeded in jettisoning all mythical elements and in formulating cosmic hypotheses (such as those of atoms and molecules) that are quite close to present-day thinking.

Ancient science (particularly biology) did not come to a standstill with Aristotle. After Alexander the center of Greek intellectual life was Alexandria and a famous library was set up there, containing the whole treasure of acquired wisdom. This library, like so much else, has not survived.

However, it was in Alexandria that Greek thought became adulterated through contact with oriental mysticism. But progress was nevertheless to continue along a truly scientific path for some generations in one particular domain—medicine. The Alexandrian doctors (the most noteworthy of them were Erophilus and Erasistratus) practiced dissection of the human body, and great progress was made in anatomy, especially that of the nervous and the circulatory systems. It appears that these doctors even conducted experiments on living people. These works, too, have been lost and are only known to us through references made by Galen and others.

Galen

A new name was added to the prestige of this school in the second century A.D. Galen (130—200) was a doctor in Pergamum, a city that the Attalus kings had raised to be the rival of Alexandria and that was also endowed with a huge library. Both physician and surgeon, Galen was the author of numerous works, only part of which have come down to us. These formed a vast medical encyclopedia, with eclectic tendencies, that remained the basic medical reference work until after the Renaissance. Galen had dissected numerous mammals, among them the elephant and some monkeys. His physiology was based on sound experimentation (he even practiced vivisection), and he may be termed the creator of nervous physiology, in which sphere he amended the conceptions of Aristotle considerably. "The nerves," Galen said, "act as leads and supply the muscles with strength that has its source in the brain." He produced states of paralysis by cutting nerves and spinal marrow; he demonstrated that the arteries contain blood and not air; and he perceived the distinction between arterial and venous blood. Great innovator though he was, Galen did not succeed in emancipating himself from the ideas of Aristotle, and he allowed himself to be blinded by the principle of final causes and by animism; he was likewise misled by overindulgence in a priori reasoning and in dialectics. The system he built up was therefore a dogmatic one, which overshadowed the bulk of his observations and experiments and falsified their true significance. For example, Galen's preconceived ideas prevented him from analyzing correctly the function of the heart and led him to affirm, in the face of patent reality, that imaginary pores exist between the two ventricles, passing through the wall that separates them. This error, following Aristotle's doctrine, led him to believe that the essential principle, the "pneuma" or breath of life, is thus able to pass from one ventricle to the other. Galen is nevertheless the creator of the experimental method in physiology, and his work represents the apogee of ancient biology. His system was to exercise a tyrannical sway over science until the early seventeenth century.

The science of botany, already highly developed by Aristotle and Theophrastus, made further progress during antiquity thanks to its therapeutic applications. At the time of Nero, Dioscorides, a Greek doctor serving in the Roman armies, wrote a medical treatise in which he propounded the properties of more than six hundred species of plants; this book also remained a reference work until modern times.

Ancient Greece may therefore be regarded as the mother of the biological sciences, progressing a considerable way with them. Rome added nothing to the store, producing only a few uncritical compilers like Pliny the Elder, or philosophers who had assimilated Greek thought and reproduced it in various forms. Such a one was Lucretius, whose philosophical poem *De natura rerum* is mainly a reflection of the views of Epicurus and contains some remarkably modern insights into the evolution of nature.

The gradual decay of the Greco-Roman world soon dried up the spring of progress, and ancient science collapsed when the Empire fell to the barbarians. This forward march was not to be resumed until the sixteenth century, when the Renaissance resurrected the thinking of classical antiquity.

2 / THE RENAISSANCE AND THE REAWAKENING OF GREEK SCIENCE

The collapse of the Roman Empire was more the result of intellectual decadence and the influence of Christianity than of direct action by the barbarians. As men ceased to be inquisitive about nature and began to indulge in excessive empty rhetoric, the science of ancient Greece fell into a deep sleep. Byzantium provided an asylum for its slumber, and it was from Byzantium that it eventually began its journey back toward the West. The Middle Ages were the era of theology. They borrowed the methods of reasoning of the Greek philosophers; these methods were now enlisted in the service of the faith and upon them was laid the cornerstone of medieval culture, scholasticism.

But, even before the Renaissance, the science of the ancients had found another vehicle, Arabic science, which conveyed it, first to Damascus and Baghdad, then to Cordova in Spain. The Arab scholars, like

Avicenna (980—1037) and Averroes (1120—1198), admired and annotated Aristotle's work. The books of these Arab philosophers were translated by Spanish Jews, then from Hebrew into Latin at the instigation of the archbishops of Toledo. Aristotle was then annotated by the great Christian scholars Michael Scotus, Albertus Magnus and Saint Thomas Aquinas; and Aristotelian biology is the foundation of the thirteenth-century compilations, like those by Albertus Magnus, Thomas Cantimpratensis (*De naturis rerum*) and Vincentius Bellovacensis, Vincent of Beauvais (*Speculum majus tripartitum*). These works are of great importance but are lacking in direct study of nature.

It was likewise Arabic medicine that handed on Greek medicine, principally through the School of Salerno, from the tenth to the thirteenth century. At the beginning of the twelfth century a synthesis of the work of this school, the *Regimen Sanitatis Salernitanum*, was composed in hexameters. It was Arabic medicine that inspired the founding of the medical faculty at Montpellier during the twelfth century. The school was to be a powerful entity until the late eighteenth century. Surgery encountered opposition from the Church and only began to take its first painful steps at the end of the Middle Ages. A return to the direct observation of nature and a reaction against the scholastic mentality came with the Renaissance and resulted from first-hand acquaintance with the writings of the Greek scientists. The Collège Royal (today called Collège de France), founded in Paris by Francis I (1530), underlined the reaction of free thinkers against the University (and especially the Sorbonne, the Faculty of Theology), which was a slave to scholasticism.

But this movement, from which our modern outlook was to emerge, was no complete and immediate liberation. While freeing knowledge from the scholastic mold, the Renaissance simultaneously subjugated it to the tyrannical authority of antiquity, which for a long time hung like a thick curtain in front of real nature. Any theory put forward as a result of direct observation was received suspiciously and even proscribed if it contradicted the authority of the ancients. Aristotle and Galen thus become obstacles in the way of progress in biology.

The Italian universities were the protagonists of the Scientific Renaissance. From them, it spread to France, Holland, Germany and England. The three great paths that were first pioneered in biology were anatomy, botany and zoology.

Anatomy

Anatomy is based on the dissection of the human corpse. This practice long remained clandestine, or was allowed only on a very small scale, because of the hostility of the Church, which regarded dissection as opposed to the whole dogma of resurrection. Thus, before the sixteenth century, dissection was often carried out on bodies stolen from graves or removed from gallows. These difficulties began to ease gradually from the fourteenth century on, and the science of anatomy slowly grew. It was sometimes practiced by artists, such as Leonardo da Vinci. The early treatises of anatomy were essentially annotated editions of Galen; the most celebrated is that by Mundinus, a professor at Bologna from 1315 to 1326. In France, the first anatomy amphitheatre was that of Montpellier, built in 1556 by Rondelet on the model of those in Italian universities. In the sixteenth century several famous anatomists worked in Paris, among them Gunther von Andernach, Jacques Dubois (Sylvius), Charles Estienne and Michael Servetus. The latter was burned at the stake in 1553 in Geneva on Calvin's orders. The great Italian anatomists of this time were Fallopio, Realdo Colombo, Botal, Varolio, Fabricius of Aquapendente and above all Vesalius. The latter, a native of Brussels, became a professor at Padua. The plates of his famous treatise, *De humani corporis fabrica*, were drawn by Etienne de Calcar, one of Titian's best pupils. Vesalius corrected many of Galen's mistakes—which were due to the latter's use of monkeys rather than men for dissection. But these corrections unleashed storms of abuse and insult on Vesalius himself. There was nothing academic about scientific controversy in the sixteenth century! The authority of the ancients was so great that the adversaries of Vesalius claimed that his disagreements with Galen could be explained by the fact that the structure of man must have changed since the days of ancient Greece. This absurdity is characteristic; it reveals the Renaissance state of mind and the obstacles that lay in the way of unprejudiced observation. Vesalius had recognized and proclaimed the non-existence of the pores in the interventricular wall of the heart, a claim that had earned him widespread scorn and criticism. But he had contradicted Galen only timidly and reluctantly: his judgment was as befogged as that of Galen himself, penetrating observer though he was, by Aristotelian doctrines on life in general.

More than a century of argument and discussion elapsed before the true facts about the circulation of the blood were established. This wrangling provides a good example of the difficulties that faced modern thinkers when they contradicted the authority of the ancients. By about 1550 Michael Servetus had discovered and understood pulmonary circulation. His conclusions brought him to the stake, in spite of his remaining a Galenist. Although there were no pores in the wall between the ventricles, Servetus admitted that a "life spirit" was able to transude it; thus he avoided a complete reversal of the master's doctrine. Without quoting Servetus, Realdo Colombo and Fabricius of Aquapendente in their turn both established the facts of pulmonary circulation.

But the whole story of circulation had to wait for William Harvey. His famous demonstration of the theory, *Exercitationes de motu cordis et sanguinis in animalibus*, was published in Frankfurt in 1628, but not without elaborate precautions for the safety of the author and only after years of controversy and opposition in the London College of Physicians. Vivisection had enabled Harvey to analyze all the movements of the heart, to ascertain that the pulse is due to the pumping of blood through the arteries, and to prove by ingenious experiments that the blood is forced outward through the arteries by the heart, to which it returns via the veins. It was not until 1661 that Malpighi, working at Bologna with a microscope, first witnessed the passage of the blood through the capillaries, thus closing the artery-vein circuit.

Harvey's discovery is one of the most significant milestones in biology, both for the facts it revealed and for the scientific attitude of mind. At the same time the discovery of the lymphatic system was begun by Aselli in Pavia (1622) and completed in Montpellier by Pecquet (1647), a few additional facts being added in the following years by Ruedbeck and Bartholin. In 1669 Lower proved by his experiments in artificial respiration that it was the influence of air in the lungs that caused the color change of blood, a phenomenon that had long been known but not understood.

This slow scientific revolution, taking place amid violent polemics and against tenacious resistance, was echoed in seventeenth-century literature, especially in the fun that Molière poked at the medical profession. Indeed, the Paris Medical Faculty was among those most obstinately opposed to new ideas. In Paris, the anatomist Riolan staunchly championed Galenism, and the founding of the Jardin du Roi (now the Natural History Museum) by Louis XIII was as great a victory for the modern mind as that of the Collège de France had been. At the Jardin there was enlightened teaching of anatomy while, at the Faculty, intellectual servitude persisted.

Botany

Botany developed on similar lines to anatomy during the sixteenth century. Here again, the Arabs had been responsible for transmitting the knowledge of the ancients to the Middle Ages. The humanists of the Renaissance revived the Greek science of botany and launched a move to find and identify the plants of the ancient pharmacopoeia, with particular reference to the "simples" or medicinal herbs. Compilations going back to the late Middle Ages have been found, as in the case of anatomy. In the sixteenth century the spirit of observation came to the fore and the examination of flora was undertaken, mainly by physicians. In France there was Jean Ruel (Ruellius, 1479—1531); in Germany, Otto Brunfels, with his *Herbarum verae icones* (1530); Jerome Bock (Tragus, 1458—1554), who published his *Neues Kräuterbuch* at Strasbourg in 1539; and Leonard Fuchs, physician, anatomist and professor at Tübingen, who, in 1542 at Basel, edited his *De stirpium historia*, containing descriptions and illustrations drawn from nature of 500 plants of South-

ern Germany, arranged in alphabetical order. Rondelet
gave the impetus that made a great botanical center of
Montpellier. Most of the great botanists of the sixteenth century studied there, among them Charles de
L'Ecluse (Clusius, 1526—1609), and from Arras,
Mathieu de L'Obel (Lobelius, 1538—1616), both physicians who made botanical explorations of the Montpellier region. Daleschamps (1513—1588) from Caen
covered the same ground; Platter from Zurich; Jean
and Gaspard Bauhin from Basel (the latter wrote *Pinax
theatri botanici*, dealing with 6,000 plant species,
arranged in natural families). In Italy, Cesalpino
(1519—1603), a professor at Pisa and physician to
Clement VIII, published the sixteen books of his *De
Plantis* in Florence (1583), the first fifteen on descriptive botany, the sixteenth on general botany, much
impregnated with Aristotelian doctrine and, in particular, with final causes. In this book the plant is conceived as an upside-down animal, the roots corresponding to the head and the soul having its seat where stem
and root meet; the flower petals are modified foils and
serve to protect the fruit or embryo.

Botanical gardens came into vogue and were set up
at Padua (1544), Pisa (1547) and Bologna (1567).
Rondelet cultivated plants in a private garden at Montpellier, but in 1593 Henry IV issued an edict creating
a chair of anatomy and botany as well as a new botanical garden with Richer de Belleval as its director. This
garden made a brilliant reputation for itself in the
seventeenth and eighteenth centuries and still exists

today. It was the physician Jean Héroard who persuaded Louis XIII in 1626 to found the Jardin du Roi in Paris. Its first administrator was Guy de La Brosse; in 1635 this institution was established in its present site in the Saint-Victor district. Exotic as well as indigenous plants are cultivated there, and the speciality is North American flora. The discovery of the New World was, incidentally, an important factor in the rise to prominence of the biological sciences. The Jardin du Roi became the main center of scientific life in eighteenth-century Paris.

Zoology

Progress in zoology kept pace with that in anatomy and botany. Observation of nature began to cast off the chains of myth and established authority, and by the sixteenth century was gradually resuming its rightful place as the spearhead of science. The solid zoological foundation left by Aristotle had already been debased by fables and superstition during the period of antiquity. Pliny's *Natural History* and Aelianus' *Treatise on the Nature of Animals* give ample evidence of this. These two works inspired and guided thinkers throughout the Middle Ages and until the sixteenth century, when voyages of exploration reaffirmed the importance of observation. After working as a compiler, the Frenchman Pierre Gilles (1490—1551) traveled to the Levant and wrote descriptions of various animals, pub-

lished posthumously. Pierre Belon (1517—1563) of Le
Mans and Guillaume Rondelet (1507—1566) of Montpellier proved themselves true zoologists; the former
explored the Eastern Mediterranean and published a
series of works based on his own observations, mainly
of marine animals. His *Histoire de la Nature des
Oiseaux,* which appeared in 1555, compares the skeleton of a bird with that of various mammals, including
man, and is thus a forerunner of comparative anatomy.
He also studied the development of the hen's egg and
scotched many fables on the subject. Rondelet is particularly noteworthy for his remarkable ichthyology,
*Libri de piscibus marinis, in quibus verae piscium
effigiae expressae sunt* (1558). Both these men had the
same sort of questing mind. Rondelet, like Belon,
traveled extensively, personally collecting and dissect-
ing material. His descriptions and illustrations are suffi-
ciently accurate for us to identify with certainty the
300 or so species of fish that he saw. Though the work
of a true naturalist, this book still made concessions to
the ancients and even sometimes to legend. Rondelet
also tackled the study of marine invertebrates, in his
Universae aquatilium historia pars altera (1555), in
which descriptions of quite rare forms, such as the
Argonaut, are found. An Italian contemporary,
Salviani, also published an ichthyology. Charles de
L'Ecluse, at that time a professor at Leyden University,
also described some exotic animals *(Exoticorum libri X,*
1605), among them the armadillo, the emu, birds of
paradise, the dodo (now extinct) and the king crab. In

Switzerland, Conrad Gesner was the author of an enormous zoological encyclopedia that was unfinished at his death in 1565. It was followed, half a century later, by a similar work by Aldrovande of Bologna.

These massive and heavy tomes attempted to incorporate everything that had been written from Pliny's day up to Rondelet and Belon; in spite of their bulk, the numerous successive editions prove how successful they were. They do not, however, represent any real progress, but are rather a reflection of the spirit of the past in the light of modern tendencies. Not even the early part of the seventeenth century brought any essential progress in zoology. Such works as appeared were mostly summaries of existing knowledge; e.g. *Histoire des Insectes*, by Thomas Moufet (1634), which forms a sequel to Gesner, and *Theatrum universale animalium*, by Johnston. Journeys to distant places resulted in works about exotic fauna; thus *Historia naturalis Brasiliae*, by the Dutchmen Pison and Marcgraff, and the book on entomology by a woman, Marie-Sybille de Mérian (1647—1717), who had lived for five years in Surinam (Dutch Guiana).

All these efforts represent nothing more than the foundations of an edifice that began to rise rapidly in the latter half of the seventeenth century.

Before leaving the Renaissance and the period that immediately followed it, mention should be made of Bernard Palissy (1510—1589), a self-educated man of great intellectual integrity who was not impregnated with classical culture. His interest embraced all aspects of nature and art; in his work he entertainingly opposes reality and accepted thought, personifying each under the names "Theory" and "Practice." He touched on many branches of science and made a particularly useful zoological survey of his province of Saintonge. To satisfy the curiosity of his contemporaries, he opened a little museum in Paris, in which was displayed a variety of material all collected and labeled by himself. This collection contained some fossils. Generally speaking, the ancients, and even Gesner, had regarded fossils as mere freaks of nature. Like Fracastor and Leonardo da Vinci, Palissy recognized them as animal remains, especially of marine shellfish, and he concluded that the seas must have moved; thus he ranks as a precursor of geology and paleontology.

3 / THE DEVELOPMENT OF MODERN BIOLOGY IN THE 17TH AND 18TH CENTURIES

Descartes

By about 1650, the efforts to liberate thought from the authority of the ancients were meeting with more and more success. Descartes (1596—1650) dealt one of the final blows with his *Discours de la Méthode* (1636) and attempted to reduce the conception of the universe to the basic principles of extension, divisibility and mobility. He was interested in anatomy and contributed to the acceptance of Harvey's discovery of circulation of the blood. He produced a comprehensive physiology, based on his theory of mechanics and explained in his *Description du corps humain* (1648). The body is a mechanism fueled by heat. Blood conveys this fuel to the brain, which it leaves again as rarefied air, the "animal spirits," to travel through the nerves to the muscles. These animal spirits dilate the brain and make it receptive to impressions of exterior objects and to those of the soul. (Descartes draws a clear distinction between the material body and the immaterial soul.) This a priori deduction contains some innovations but is not based on observation and is not free from the influence of Aristotle and Galen. Descartes' mechanical theory has exercised a considerable and long-lasting influence on modern thought; but it is nevertheless more in the nature of bold intuition than positive acquisition.

Microscopic Observation: Leeuwenhoek

Toward the middle of the seventeenth century a new method of observation was introduced, which soon considerably widened the observer's vision. This was the use of enlarging lenses (the magnifying glass and the compound microscope), a result of the researches of Galileo. It was an innovation of capital importance. Other new techniques were soon to be a great source of progress; one such was the injection into the blood vessels of solidifiable and colored liquids. This process was invented about 1660 by Boyle and by Pecquet, and was developed further by Swammerdam and by Ruysch. It brought about great progress in the science of anatomy.

Robert Hooke (1637—1703) and Nehemiah Grew (1627—1711) in England, and Marcello Malpighi (1628—1694) in Italy, made fundamental discoveries about the structure of plants by using a magnifying glass; with the same instrument Swammerdam (1637—1680) studied the lower animals and Van Leeuwenhoek, an observer of outstanding accuracy and skill, was able to explore a whole new world.

Malpighi was the creator of microscopic anatomy. In 1661 he made direct observations of the passage of the blood through the pulmonary capillaries and through the blood vessels in the wing of a bat, thus verifying the complete theory about circulation. He investigated the structure of the glands and of the skin, discovered the corpuscles of touch, examined the structure of the nerves and the brain, of the kidney and the viscera. He made detailed observations and illustrative plates of the development of the hen's egg. He investigated the anatomy of insects and made his notable discovery of their tracheal system; he established the cellular structure of plants and created other techniques, like the maceration and coction of tissues. He was the forerunner of histology.

Swammerdam was unexcelled in his skill at dissection and at perceiving minute details of anatomy. His observations were remarkably extensive, especially on the lower animals. He died young after lapsing into mysticism and destroying some of his own manuscripts. Fortunately, many of the remainder were saved and sold, eventually to be published in 1737 by Boerhaave under the title *Biblia Naturae*. Swammerdam manufactured his own magnifying lenses. He was a skilled initiator of the injection technique, a pioneer of detailed anatomy and of the study of insect metamorphosis. His experiments on the frog make him also one of the forerunners of embryology.

Leeuwenhoek[1] has often been called the father of protozoology and of bacteriology and even, in more general terms, of the whole of microscopic biology, both animal and vegetable. And yet he was not a professional scientist! A burgher of Delft, he had been drawn to microscopic observation by his need as a draper to count the threads of his fabrics. He made his own lenses, more than 400 of them, some with a linear enlargement of up to 160. With these rudimentary means he was able to discover and interpret a world of tiny creatures, even including bacteria. He observed them particularly inside capillary tubes and explored a great variety of media, like water, various infusions, the contents of the organs, etc. His findings are reported in letters that, from 1673 until his death in 1723, he addressed to the Royal Society of London, writing in his native Dutch, the only language he knew. These letters have been translated into Latin or English.[2]

[1]Clifford Dobell, *Antony Van Leeuwenhoek and His Little Animals* (New York: Dover Publications). This work is extremely well documented on original sources and deals admirably with the personality and work of Leeuwenhoek as well as with the intellectual climate that surrounded this work and the origins of the microscope.

[2]These letters, numbering more than 200, have almost all been published in the *Philosophical Transactions* of the Royal Society. They have, moreover, been collected (except the first 27, some of which are still unpublished) in four volumes, published first in Dutch, then in Latin (*Opera omnia, seu arcania Naturae, ope exactissimorum microscopiorum detecta,* etc., Leyden, 1722).

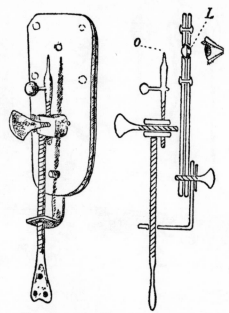

Fig. 1. Leeuwenhoek's microscope (single lens). *Left,* side view of the instrument. *Right,* section showing the principle. *L,* lens; *O,* position of object to be examined. (After Dobell.)

His compatriots Regnier De Graaf and Christiaan Huygens recommended him to the London Society, and he was made a member of that august body in 1680.

Leeuwenhoek laid bare a whole new world: protozoa of all groups, free-moving and parasitic, bacteria of infusions and those of the mouth, various invertebrates, such as the Rotifera. He discovered spermatozoa (spermatic animalculae) in human sperm and

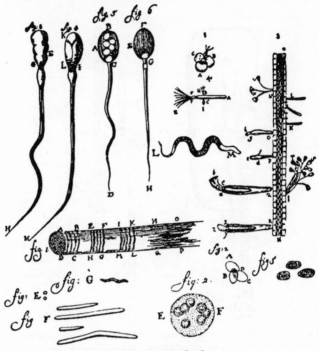

Fig. 2. Some drawings by Leeuwenhoek.

A. *Top left*, spermatozoa: *figs. 3 and 4*, dog; *figs. 5 and 6*, rabbit (letter 44, 1684).

B. Top right: *1*, duckweed (*Lemna*); *3*, duckweed root (note the cellular structure) bearing diatoms (*K-L*), vorticellae (*Carchesium NVW* and *IST*), tube-dwelling rotifers (*RXYZ* and *QABC, Melicerta*) and tube-dwelling Infusoria (*Cothurnia, PDEF* and *OGH*); *4*, hydra with reproductive bud (letter dated 25-XII-1702, *Philos. Transact. No. 283*, after Dobell).

C. *LM*, vinegar threadworm (letter 43).

D. Beneath the spermatozoa: *fig. 1*, muscular fiber of the ox (letter 34).

E. *Bottom left*: Oral bacteria; *fig. E*, micrococci; *fig. F, Leptothrix buccalis; fig. G*, spirochete (letter 39, 17-IX-1683, after Dobell).

F. *Bottom center*: *EF, Volvox* (letter 122, 2-I-1700).

G. *Bottom right*: Red blood globules; *fig. 2*, frog (letter 38); *fig. 5*, fish (letter 34).

then in a whole series of animals that he investigated. Through the Royal Society his discoveries became widely known; they were checked and discussed by men like the physician Robert Hooke and by Nehemiah Grew, and they won an international reputation for their author. Many distinguished visitors came to Delft to see his lenses and to look at the animalculae through them. These visitors included, in 1698, Tsar Peter the Great, to whom Leeuwenhoek showed the blood circulating through a tadpole's tail; the Tsar devoted two hours to these microscopic observations. From this example we may judge the stir created by the researches of Leeuwenhoek; in every sense of the work he was a self-taught man on whom the authority of the ancients had no influence, who observed and described what he had seen without prejudice, without methodical order or desire to synthesize, but with scrupulous honesty. This "amateur" exercised a profound and durable influence on biology.

Réaumur and Experimentation

Great though Leeuwenhoek's contributions were, biological science owes even more to Réaumur (1683—1757), one of the creators of the experimental method in biology and one of the most inquisitive, sagacious and balanced minds in the history of science. The son of a magistrate, Réaumur received a broad intellectual education with particular emphasis on mathematics and physics. At the age of twenty-three he moved to Paris and entered the Académie des Sciences as a junior mechanician, attached to Varignon; five years later he was elected a member of this academy and for the next fifty years, by his own research and by the encouragement he gave to others, his influence was enormous, not only in Paris but throughout Europe. He was, first and foremost, a great engineer and physicist, the creater of manifold inventions in metallurgy, in the making of porcelain, and in numerous mechanical problems. He perfected the thermometer, introduced the use of refrigerating mixtures, etc. A royal pension of 12,000 francs rewarded his services, and Réaumur was then able to lead a secure but hard-working existence in Paris and on his country estates. With perfect serenity of mind, he devoted himself to the observation of animals in the light of experimentation. He is one of the founders of physiology and, in a more general sense, the creator of biological ethology. By reason of his education Réaumur had a positive mind and was not prone to losing himself in speculation. He was a freethinker within the frame of orthodoxy and was not averse to accepting a providential arrangement of nature. It was on this basis that he analyzed the details of nature; his sole preoccupation was exact description. To this end he made intuitive use of the experimental method, which explains why his work has dated much less quickly than that of some others. The problems he investigated and for which he found more or less complete solutions are those with which we are still faced today; indeed, even in those cases where great progress has been made since his day, Réaumur's solutions are still very modern in character. During a lifetime of continuous scientific research, Réaumur made tremendous contributions to our knowledge of invertebrates (or "insects," as they were called at that time). He published his findings in very many articles in the transactions of the Académie des Sciences and in the six volumes of his *Mémoires pour servir à l'histoire des Insectes* (1734—1742). These works are still a fruitful source for the researcher, as are others that are still unpublished. After 1742 Réaumur became more preoccupied with other branches of science, and he left a whole series of articles incomplete and unpublished. It had been his intention to use this material for the concluding volumes of his history of insects.[3]

[3]These unpublished manuscripts are among the archives of the Académie des Sciences. An eminent American biologist, W. M. Wheeler, brought to light in 1926 a magnificent dissertation on the *Story of Ants*. In this work Réaumur proved to be fifty years ahead of his time. The editing of Volume VII of the *Mémoires sur les Insectes* (almost finished by Réaumur) was completed in 1928. The present author wrote an introduction for this volume, which unfortunately has still not made its appearance in public. Réaumur had also written a *Histoire des Arts* (dealing with industrial processes), for which he had more than 150 plates engraved. These were misappropriated and used, without his authorization, for the publication of the *Encyclopédie*. In a letter to Albert de Haller he wrote: "I preferred to seem to know nothing about it, rather than disturb my peace of mind by reclaiming my property."

Many of Réaumur's works are even more strictly experimental and make him a precursor of physiology in the proper sense. Such are his experiments on the digestion of birds (he extracted their gastric juice by means of a sponge tied to a thread), his researches on regeneration, his treatise on the hatching of hen's eggs by artificial heat, etc.

Furthermore, he was a great teacher, who directed and encouraged a host of scholars all over Europe. He had no less than twenty-eight correspondents attached to him, under the provisions of the Académie. Among these was Charles Bonnet of Geneva, who, after reading *Mémoires sur les Insectes*, went on, at the age of twenty, to discover parthenogenesis in plant lice (1742); Abraham Tremblay at The Hague, who discovered how hydra are able to multiply when divided; Charles de Geer of Stockholm, who, like his master, also published some articles on insects; and many travelers to tropical lands, who sent him specimens, thermometric observations, etc. The position occupied by Réaumur is one of the most eminent, not only in his own century, but in the history of biology in general.

Although inferior to Réaumur in his breadth of vision, Roesel von Rosenhof (1705—1759) made important contributions to science, observing and describing the life of many invertebrates with great accuracy and artistic sense. He was especially concerned with insects (*Insektenbelustigungen*, 4 parts, 1746—1761) and with frogs; he did not live to complete a work on lizards. His books are magnificently illustrated, but mostly rather naïve in their conception and steeped in admiration for the orderliness of nature and for its Creator.

Generation

We now reach an important period in the development of knowledge about generation and embryogeny.

At last the ghost of *spontaneous generation* was laid, at least until it was resuscitated in the nineteenth century. The ancients had almost all supported the doctrine; Aristotle, for example, held that eels are born from the slime of river beds. It was inevitable that the eel's life story remained so long mysterious; the riddle was solved only a few years ago by Johann Schmidt, who proved that eels go down to the sea to reproduce, crossing the ocean to the depths in mid-Atlantic where they lay their eggs. The eel larvae then undertake the return journey and climb up-river as *elvers*. Leeuwenhoek still believed that they began their existence in the mud of marshes. It was also assumed that flies are born spontaneously on decomposing meat, and likewise maggots in fruit.

In 1668 the Italian anatomist Redi (1626—1698), one of the best biologists of his day, settled all argument on the subject for the next century and a half. He demonstrated that it is only necessary to protect meat with gauze or place it in a sealed flask to prevent the maggots appearing. This simply prevents flies from laying eggs on it. However, he dared not go as far as denying absolutely the spontaneous generation of parasitic worms in the intestines or in the plant galls. Leeuwenhoek's discoveries of the world of microscopic animalculae added fresh weight to the idea of spontaneous generation because it was not immediately apparent how these creatures reproduced themselves. Needham, an Irish priest and a skillful zoologist, was responsible for a variety of interesting observations but believed that he had proved that Infusoria are born spontaneously. He argued that they still appear in hermetically sealed infusions or in meat juice that has been boiled and heated. Needham thought that these animalculae were formed by combinations of organic molecules, under the influence of *vegetative force*. The decomposition of organic substances was therefore the source of lower forms of life. Buffon adopted this standpoint and, using all his powers of persuasion, built a whole theory about generation upon them; organic molecules, which are present everywhere and incorruptible, join together by virtue of a *formative force* and constitute the internal matrix of the organisms and of their various parts. This quaint theory was mocked by Voltaire and Réaumur. The latter, with the help of P. de Lignac, undertook experiments that refuted Buffon. The arguments appeared in 1751 in an anonymous book (whose author was, in fact, de Lignac) published in Hamburg and entitled *Lettres à un Amériquain sur l'Histoire naturelle de M. de Buffon et sur les observations de M. Needham.* But final refutation of the theory came with the work of the priest Spallanzani, one of the greatest names in science in the eighteenth century. With carefully conducted experiments that remind us of Pasteur's, he proved that, given sufficient heat and effective sealing, the infusions do not become alive with organisms. To which Needham simply objected that heating destroyed the vegetative force.

Knowledge about generation in the proper sense made important progress in the seventeenth and eighteenth centuries, and this progress throws significant light on prevailing ideas. Here again the first name mentioned must be Harvey and his *Exercitationes de generatione animalium* (1651). In this book he describes the development of the chicken embryo, and it is very noteworthy that he opposes the idea that a miniature chicken already exists in the egg; like Aristotle, he rightly held that the development was progressive. He gave the name *epigenesis* to his idea, which opposes that of *preformation.* Harvey was physician to Charles I and, with the King's permission, he slaughtered and dissected some of the deer in the grounds of Windsor Park. Carefully noting the number of days and weeks following mating, he discovered very young embryos in the horns of the uterus. These embryos were in various stages of development and not yet fixed to the uterus wall. He concluded that the first product of conception is invariably some kind of egg.[4]

Holland, which produced so many eminent men of science at this period, was the home of a young anatomist, Regnier de Graaf (1641—1673). In spite of his early death his accomplishments were considerable, among them his claim to have discovered the *initial egg* of mammals. He made a very detailed study[5] of female genitalia and described the transparent and turgescent vesicles on the human ovaries and on those of various animals (cow, ewe, rabbit). These vesicles are filled with liquid and they burst at a given moment. De Graaf interpreted them as being the eggs (ova). They are, in fact, what is known today as Graafian

[4]The frontispiece of Harvey's *Exercitationes* (Fig. 3) represents Jupiter opening a round box, the egg, which bears the inscription *Ex ovo omnia*; various creatures are emerging from this box. This inscription has generally been falsely transcribed into the formula *Omne vivum ex ovo*, which, although a good summary of Harvey's thought, is not strictly authentic. At the end of Part I of this book, Harvey respectfully discusses the ideas of his former master Fabricius of Aquapendente and states very clearly: *Nos autem (ut ex dicendis constabit) omnia omnino animalia, etiam vivipara atque hominem ideo ipsum ex ovo progigni, primosque eorum conceptus e quibus foetus fiunt ova quaedam esse, ut et semina plantarum.* This text reveals how deep was Harvey's intuition of reality. Unlike his master, he rejected spontaneous generation and considered that those cases attributed to it are, in fact, explained by a difference between parents and offspring (*aequivoca, ut aiunt, generatione a parentibus sui dissimilibus*).

[5]R. de Graaf, *De Mulierum organis generationi inservientibus Tractatus novus*, etc. (Leyden, 1672). This treatise has sixteen chapters; the twelfth is devoted to the ovaries of woman, and the sixteenth to rabbits.

follicles, and the egg proper is inside them; this fact was not proved until 1827 by Karl von Baer, working on the dog, but it is interesting to note how close De Graaf was to the complete discovery; indeed, he might

Fig. 3. Frontispiece of the original edition of *Exercitationes de generatione animalium* (London, 1651).

well have discovered the whole truth if he had lived longer. He got as far as observing that these vesicles burst and leave a cicatricial body (the yellow body, or corpus luteum) on the ovary (Fig. 4, *I*, *BB*). De Graaf made a most praiseworthy experimental study[6] of these phenomena and had the lucky intuition to choose the rabbit as his subject. It is now known that, in these animals, the breaking of the follicles depends on the act of mating. By methodically killing doe rabbits before mating and after mating at graduated intervals (½ hour, 6, 24, 27, 48, 52, 72 hours; then each following day), he observed the bursting of the follicles on the ovary[7] and, from the third day onward, he found young embryos (which he called *ova*) in the uterus; these increased progressively in size and were drawn by De Graaf in the various stages of their development (Plates XXVI and XXVII).

[6]Chapter XVI begins thus: "As all the facts reported in the preceding chapters cannot be verified *de visu* in the human subject, I carried out my dissections on animals, choosing those kinds that I could procure in good numbers, in which the time of mating could be noted exactly and that produce several fetuses at the same time, so that I could observe in one what might escape me in another. These considerations made me choose the doe rabbit."

[7]"Fifty-two hours after mating, we examined a doe rabbit in which we found in one testicle (ovary) one and in the other four unchanged [*immutatos*] follicles; having dissected them, we found a glandular-like substance in them, with a small cavity in the middle; on finding no significant quantity of liquid in the latter, we began to wonder if the fluid of the follicles, which is enclosed within the wall, may not be discharged by the bursting of that wall" (*Op. cit,* Chap. XVI).

These far-reaching discoveries were, however, obscured during the eighteenth century by endless arguments concerning the essential nature of the development that takes place; some favored the notion of *preformation* (complete formation from the very outset of the individual within the seed), others supported *epigenesis* (progressive formation, as outlined by Harvey). The conception of preformation was strengthened, quite logically, by Swammerdam's theory of the growth of already existing parts; this notion was suggested by a study of the chrysalis, inside which he had found a fully formed butterfly. Many maintained that this continuity applied to every generation, past, present and future. Common sense and direct observation struggled against such ideas for more than a century. An irrefutable success in this campaign was registered in 1759 by a young German doctor, G. F. Wolff (1733—1794), in his doctorate thesis *Theoria generationis*. This was a study of the successive stages in the development of a chicken and produced evidence of the progressive formation of the embryo's structure, just as the protagonists of epigenesis had contended. But even this failed to convince some very illustrious contemporaries; the physiologist Albert de Haller rejected the thesis out of hand in favor of the theory of preformation, and he had the support of such eminent scientists as Charles Bonnet and Spallanzani.[8]

---

[8]Shortly before his death in 1832 Cuvier was still upholding the preformation theory.

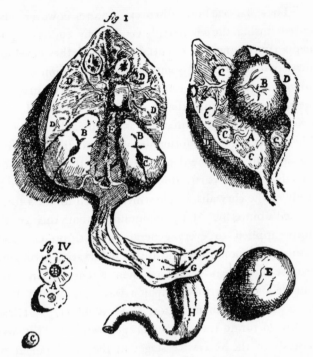

Fig. 4. *Top left:* fig. *I,* longitudinal section of a cow's ovary; *BB,* corpus luteum (*glandulosa substantia quae post ovi expulsionem in testibus reperitur, per media divisa*); *CC, Cavitas in qua ovum contentum fuit, fere obsoleta; DD,* follicles (*ova diversae magnitudinis in ovario contenta*); *E,* blood vessels; *F, H,* Fallopian tube; *G,* opening of the tube.

Bottom left: fig. *IV,* follicle from a ewe's ovary before the expulsion of the egg (*prout ovum adhuc continebat*); *B, Locus ex quo ovum exemptum est; ovum ex eo exemptum* (judging by the size, it is unlikely that this is in fact the egg).

Top right: Cow's ovary opened lengthwise; *B, Ovum maximum seu maturum* [ripe follicle] *in testicula adhuc contentum; D,* Dartos' membrane.

Bottom right: E, ripe follicle extracted from the ovary (R. de Graaf, *loc. cit.,* pls. XIV and XV).

Another field of argument was opened up by Leeuwenhoek's discovery of spermatic animalculae or spermatozoa. Some, the *spermatists,* saw in these the actual germ or seed; the preformationists held that the fully developed animal was present in them, in spite of their minuteness;[9] according to others, the *ovists,* the seed proper was provided by the female and the spermatic animalculae only served to stimulate, by their wriggling, the exhalation of the *spirits* into the seminal fluid, *aura seminalis.* This conception was in harmony with Aristotle and Descartes.

In the eighteenth century an endless series of controversies and theses resulted from these conflicting and sometimes peculiar conceptions; the real explanation

[9]Hartsoeker (1656-1729), who claimed to have discovered spermatozoa before Leeuwenhoek, published his views about generation at the end of his *Essays on Dioptrics* (1694). Alongside some interesting intuitions about fertilization (the spermatozoon penetrating into the egg through a pore and monospermy), he believed in preformation and continuity of development, and he illustrated (Fig. 5, *1*) the theoretical structure of the spermatozoon, as he imagined it to be, with a fully formed homunculus already inside.

This claim provoked a so-called verification that was, in fact, merely a hoax, but presented so seriously that most people were taken in by it. François de Plantade, secretary of the Montpellier Académie des Sciences, wrote a letter in Latin under the name Dalenpatius (anagram of Plantadeius), which was published in *Nouvelles de la République des Lettres* (Amsterdam, Vol. II, April, 1699). In this letter he gravely relates that he was surprised to observe, under the microscope, a spermatozoon cast its skin for a tiny, ready-made man to emerge (Fig. 5, 2-3: ... *clare ostendit ambas tibias, crura, pectus, gemina brachia et exutum altius protractum caput ad instar cucullae obnubebat. Sexuum discrimina, prae exiguitate, nosci non quita sunt*).

was not generally accepted until the nineteenth century. The position adopted by Spallanzani, in spite of his admirable experiments, will illustrate how thick was the veil cast over men's minds by preconceived ideas and theories.

Fig. 5. *1*, theoretical spermatozoid according to Hartsoeker; *2* and *3*, spermatozoid as described by Dalenpatius.

Spallanzani (1729—1799), as well as contributing to discussion on spontaneous generation, produced some noteworthy contributions to biology and was also the author of remarkable works on mineralogy and geology. But he is primarily remembered as one of the great figures of biology and as a creator of the experimental method. He made major contributions to the study of digestion, circulation, regeneration, reviviscence and reproduction. In his work on reproduction, he had the great foresight to choose amphibia (frogs and toads); in mating, the male climbs onto the female's back and sprinkles sperm on the eggs as they are being laid. Spallanzani devised shrewd and logical experiments in order to determine the conditions under which the eggs did or did not develop; he demonstrated that there was no development if the fertilizing power of the male fluid was withheld or if the eggs were not allowed to come into direct contact with this fluid (he achieved this result by covering the male's underparts in tiny waterproof pants); if the male fluid was filtered beforehand, then the liquid collected on the filter had the power to fertilize even when diluted in enormous proportions, but it lost this property if heated beyond a certain temperature. These logical tests should have led him to the conclusion that the spermatozoa are the fertilizing elements and that they must have access to the egg if it is to develop. And yet Spallanzani did not draw this conclusion, because he was too befogged by the concept of preformation, which he shared with his friends Haller and Bonnet. He held that, at the time of laying, the eggs are already *fetuses,* in which the young animal already exists as such, without being apparent. The role of the seminal fluid was merely to *manifest* it. This example shows how blinded by prevailing conceptions an eminent intellect can be. It was not until fifty years later, in 1824, that Prévost and Dumas, in Geneva, carried out similar experiments (independently of Spallanzani) and this time deduced the fertilizing role of the spermatozoa; even then some voices were raised in contradiction. Spallanzani's shortsightedness is all the more surprising when we remember that his experiments on amphibians led him to inject sperm into the genital passage of a bitch, thereby achieving fertilization by artificial insemination.

Among eighteenth-century research on generation, mention must be made again of Charles Bonnet's brilliant discovery in 1742 of parthenogenesis in plant lice.

This brief summary reveals how heavy were the chains of arbitrary and erroneous theoretical conceptions upon the feet / of direct observation and experimentation. Thus the eighteenth century only takes us part of the way toward complete understanding of generation; one vital notion was still lacking at that time: the exact value of the reproductive elements.

General Physiology: Lavoisier

We have already seen how some eighteenth-century naturalists, notably Réaumur and Spallanzani, used experimental methods and thus laid the foundations of physiology. Some surgeons also employed experimental techniques. In 1710, Pourfour du Petit, after triphining, damaged the cerebral cortex of various animals on one side, thus paralyzing the opposite side of the body. With the aid of hypodermic needles, Lorry explored the medulla oblongata and thus discovered the vital node. But these are isolated cases. It was not until the end of the eighteenth century that physiology was ready to advance rapidly under the influence of a man of genius, Lavoisier (1743—1794),[10] who was not only the creator of modern chemistry but also the initiator of general physiology. It was he who proved in 1777 that, contrary to the doctrines of antiquity, which still persisted, respiration is not designed to cool the

[10]Cf. Ed. Grimaux, *Lavoiser (1743-1749), d'après ses observations*, etc. (Paris, 1888).

blood but is a process of combustion effected by means of the oxygen in the air and producing carbonic acid; furthermore, the change of color of the blood corresponds to oxidation (the Englishman Lower had already seen this in 1669). These facts suggested to Lavoisier that respiration is the basis of animal heat. Collaborating with the great mathematician Laplace, and later with Séguin, he made an outstanding experimental study of this principle. He grasped the fundamental link between the functions of digestion, respiration and transpiration, which regulate body temperature and maintain the dynamic balance of the organism. He described food as the oil that supplies the lamp; without fuel the lamp would go out. These monumental findings were based on simple but strict experiments in which unfounded speculation played no part.

Lavoisier's work constitutes one of the great milestones in biology. Indeed, he would certainly have gone even further if the French Revolution had not cost him his head. He was preparing to compete for a prize offered by the Académie des Sciences (1794) before that institution was suppressed; he intended to demonstrate the fundamental mechanism of the cycle of all living matter. "Plants," he said, "derive the materials necessary for their organization from air, water and the mineral kingdom; animals feed on plants or on other animals, which, in their turn, feed on plants; finally, fermentation, putrefaction and combustion are perpetually returning to the atmosphere and to the mineral kingdom those principles that the plants and animals have borrowed from them. By what processes," he asks, "does nature operate this marvelous circulation between the three kingdoms?" The greater part of the answer to this question was provided by Pasteur in the nineteenth century.

In order to complete the picture of the period under survey, mention must be made of the progress achieved in descriptive natural history. The number of animal and plant forms known to science had been growing since the Renaissance. Europe, the New World and the tropics were gradually being explored by men in search of knowledge or gold or spices. The need to classify the newly discovered forms led, slowly but surely, toward a precise notion of *genus* and *species*. This notion took some shape in the seventeenth century with G. Bauhin, with Morrison and John Ray in England, Tournefort in France, and others. In the eighteenth century, Linnaeus (1707—1778) crowned all these efforts by defining precisely the difference between genus and species, both in zoology and in botany, and by establishing the binominal nomenclature. His system proved so appropriate and practical that it is in general use today. The tenth edition of his *Systema naturae* (1758) is universally adopted as the basis for classifying animals and plants; it has made it possible to arrange and maintain order among the enormous mass of new species still being described today.

But methodical description and nomenclature do not of themselves constitute a natural classification, in which the affinities of the species and families are established. However, great progress was made in this direction as regards botany, thanks to the work of the brothers Jussieu (Antoine, 1686—1758, and especially Bernard, 1699—1777), and of their nephew, Antoine-Laurent Jussieu, whose *Genera plantarum secundum ordines naturales disposita* (1789) was the cornerstone of nineteenth-century botany.

Some other memorable botanical discoveries were made in the eighteenth century, one of these being the mechanism of plant reproduction. Back in antiquity, Theophrastus had guessed the part played by the stamens[11] in the artificial fertilization of the palm tree (as practiced since time immemorial in the oases), and in the caprification of the fig tree. In the seventeenth century, Charles de l'Ecluse distinguished the male and female flowers of the papaw tree; Cesalpino, on the other hand, was too steeped in Aristotelian ideas to admit that sexuality was possible in plants. The role of the stamens as male organs was perceived more or less clearly by various botanists, but the crucial experiments that finally elucidated the matter were those of Camerarius of Tübingen. His findings were published under

[11]Theophrastus writes: "It is claimed that the fruit of the palm tree does not develop fully unless the female flower is sprinkled with powder from the male flower. This is a strange fact, but it reminds us of the caprification of fig trees. We could almost conclude that the female plant alone is insufficient for the complete development of the seed. But this phenomenon is no doubt not peculiar to plants of only one species; it probably exists throughout the vegetable kingdom."

the title *Epistola de sexu plantarum* in 1694. Some fifty years later, Koelreuter, of Karlsruhe, systematically practiced hybridization between species and thus laid the foundations of the science known today as genetics.

The most striking general impression of the period just reviewed is one of the extensive progress achieved from about 1650 on as a result of experimentation and direct unprejudiced observation.

4 / THE ADVANCE OF BIOLOGY FROM THE 19TH CENTURY TO THE PRESENT

By the late eighteenth century the way was clear for biology to advance at an ever-increasing pace. The geographical distribution of scientific research had steadily expanded; from fifteenth-century Italy it had reached the rest of Europe long before the nineteenth century, and in recent times American contributions have grown immeasurably in number and importance. Indeed, the United States today is able to devote almost unlimited resources to the service of science.

The scientific work of the eighteenth century could be summarized under a few great names; as this is by no means true for the nineteenth century, considerations of space will limit us to an outline of the main currents of facts and ideas, and it will not be possible to name all who have made important contributions.

It is significant that the word *biology* was coined

early in the nineteenth century. In 1802, Lamarck in France and Treviranus in Germany simultaneously made first use of the term to imply the unity of the processes of life in both the animal and vegetable kingdoms, and to suggest that the various ways of studying these kingdoms converge toward one single fundamental doctrine.

Two important tendencies, which were already in existence beforehand, were now becoming increasingly well defined. The individual branches of biology had grown more autonomous as the activities of scholars became more specialized, but biological science was advancing in two main directions. The first was toward a study of the individual structure of living organisms, *morphology* (Goethe first used the word in 1807); the second concentrated on the way animals and plants function, *physiology*. Morphology is based primarily on observation; in practice this means examination of dead and preserved specimens, and concentration on and comparison of anatomical detail, which permits the classification of organisms according to their actual affinities. The workshops of this science are the museums; these increased correspondingly in importance as morphology came to the fore.

Physiology became a fully constituted science with an agreed-upon *modus operandi* in the early nineteenth century. Physiology is essentially concerned with the experimental study of the living organism. In practice it almost invariably transcends the particular object under study to discover, through that object, mechanisms that extend to all existing organisms, or at least to sizable groups of them.

These two currents, apparently so distinct, in fact converge by the very nature of things and are complementary. Diversity fuses into unity, and today the term biology often tends to designate the zone of contact between morphology and physiology. In this zone the varied results of the former are envisaged from the unitary points of view of the latter. For the sake of clarity, however, this book will consider the two domains separately.

Morphology

All living things are constituted in a particular way, and the essential characteristics of this constitution form the basis for distinguishing between species and orders. The general inventory of animal and plant species, whether alive today or known only from fossils, is still not complete, and many new ones are described each year. But the framework is now fully drawn thanks to the hierarchy that has been gradually established between groups of varying importance: genus, family, order, class, sub-kingdom. The dividing line between genera and families may still be rather hazy, but the autonomy of the higher groupings is perfectly clear-cut because these are separated from each other by gaps of discontinuity in organization. Comparative anatomy, which is practically another term for morphology, has therefore been the foundation on which a general, rational classification of organisms has been built; this system may be termed *natural,* as it is an expression of real affinities.

We have seen how the brothers Jussieu and their cousin outlined the classification of the plant kingdom according to the simple principle of arranging distinctive characteristics in order. Their work was continued in the nineteenth century and is still being developed today. However, the problem of classifying animals was much more complex, because of their greater diversity and the insufficient knowledge about them. Indeed, many important types were not even known to science until the nineteenth century.

THE FOUNDERS OF ANIMAL MORPHOLOGY:

LAMARCK, CUVIER, ETIENNE GEOFFROY

SAINT-HILAIRE

At the end of the eighteenth century, Vicq-D'Azyr (1748—1794) in France and Kielmeyer in Germany had already undertaken the task of building up the science of animal morphology on rational principles, based particularly on the ordered arrangement of characters. This work was continued in France, Germany and England by a succession of zoologists, in the first rank of whom were Georges Cuvier (1769—1832), Etienne Geoffroy Saint-Hilaire (1772—1844) and Lamarck (1744—1829). These men may be regarded as the founders of comparative anatomy and general morphology. They formulated principles and applied them with brilliant success. Geoffroy Saint-Hilaire was particularly responsible for establishing the principle of *connections,* by which is meant the absolute constancy of the position of the organs in different animals. Knowledge of this is the fundamental clue in comparative anatomy; it led Saint-Hilaire to discern the major importance of the rudimentary organs and to deduce the outstanding value of embryogeny as a complement to, and even a basis of, anatomy. He was also the founder of teratology. He was at times guilty of developing his theories beyond the limit justified by facts. This was how he arrived at his erroneous conception that one unified plan of composition was applicable to the whole animal kingdom, so that the arthropods (insects, crustaceans) were comparable to the vertebrates. His famous argument with Cuvier on this subject (1830) was followed by all the scholars of Europe and led inevitably to the victory of his opponent.

Georges Cuvier is undeniably one of the most illustrious names in zoology. His mind was bold, clear and positive but at the same time penetrating and controlled. He attached the maximum importance to facts but was skilled in subordinating and grouping them. He possessed a wonderful talent for expounding his facts both as a professor and as a writer, and his work dominates the whole of the early nineteenth century; indeed its influence made itself felt long after that. He sketched the broad outlines for the classification of the animal kingdom, dividing it into four sub-kingdoms. These have since been subdivided as a result of increased knowledge, but they nevertheless represent an important milestone in the study of animals. Cuvier appreciated the full value of the *correlations* between the various organs: within any given group, a part of the animal's organization allows us to draw conclusions about the structure of other species and genera in that group. Thus the dentition of a mammal is sufficient means of identifying the group to which it belongs. By studying from this point of view the incomplete remains of fossilized mammals found in the Paris region, Cuvier earned for himself the right to be considered the founder of paleontology. However, even the best-established principles never have an absolute value, and, in spite of some illuminating results, the application of the correlation principle sometimes led Cuvier into errors that have since been revealed by more comprehensive documentation. But these few mistakes hardly detract from the general fruitfulness of the idea. Similarly, although Cuvier prided himself on being a positive thinker who always walked with feet firmly on the ground of facts, he nevertheless sometimes allowed himself to be carried away by his imagination, drawing unjustified conclusions without factual basis. This was the case with his famous *Discours sur les Révolutions du Globe* and his theory about sudden and general catastrophes that destroy whole faunas and thus bring about the gaps in the hierarchy of living organisms. This idea was subsequently misapplied and exaggerated by Alcide d'Orbigny.

Lamarck also made an invaluable contribution to

our knowledge of the animal kingdom, especially in the domain of the invertebrates. Cuvier and Geoffroy Saint-Hilaire had both been appointed while still young to professorships at the Muséum d'Histoire Naturelle, but Lamarck was already fifty with a fruitful career as a botanist behind him when he occupied his chair. His was an audacious and adventurous intellect, nurtured in the school of Buffon and eighteenth-century philosophy. He was wont to pursue his ideas relentlessly, without always verifying the solidity of the foundations upon which he built; thus it frequently happened that he was off the track from the beginning. He refused, for example, to accept Lavoisier's new findings in chemistry, preferring to remain faithful to earlier doctrines. In the precarious state of positive knowledge prevailing in his day, he conceived the general functioning of the organisms on bases that were often fragile to say the least, and the conclusions he drew from them were frequently out of date and almost irresponsible. This criticism will be raised again later on the subject of transformism. Nevertheless his insight into the past of our planet and the life upon it was closer to reality than Cuvier's. He was the precursor of Lyell and the theory of actualistic causes that remains the foundation of modern geology.

These three men may, by and large, be considered the founders of modern morphology in France. Meanwhile, in Germany, the philosophy of nature was about to wander off into metaphysical ideas utterly divorced from reality. For the next generation at least, the greatest names in zoology outside France follow the pathway Cuvier had mapped; these were R. Owen and T. Huxley in England, K. von Baer and J. Müller in Germany. The work of the last named tended to be more physiological than the others and was, moreover, tainted with vitalism.

THE EXPANSION OF ZOOLOGY: MARINE
ZOOLOGY AND OCEANOGRAPHY

One of the directions in which nineteenth-century zoology made most progress was the study of marine faunas. Long before 1900 a whole series of maritime expeditions had set off for the Southern Seas, especially for the Pacific. Bougainville's journey to Tahiti had aroused wide interest; likewise La Pérouse's explorations, which came to a sudden end when he disappeared in 1787, Cook's discovery of Australia, etc. Several French expeditions followed these same routes around the turn of the century and brought home much precious material for study. English zoologists were also collecting, while expeditions of various nationalities were probing into the Arctic in search of the Northwest Passage and the North Pole.

These journeys continued into the second half of the nineteenth century, and became more and more often specifically zoological in character. About 1850 the laying and maintenance of the first submarine telegraph cables had revealed the existence of a fauna that prompted the exploration of the ocean depths. The most famous and fruitful of such voyages was that of

the *Challenger* (1873—76). The United States joined
in this quest with a series of expeditions with which
the names of Dana and Agassiz (in the *Blake* and the
Albatross) are especially associated. Among the German expeditions, the most noteworthy was that of the
Valdivia, directed by C. Chun, and the *Plankton-
Expedition,* which was devoted principally to the surface fauna. Since 1900 the great expeditions have
turned their attentions to Antarctica (the *Gauss,* and
others, from Germany, the *Belgica* from Belgium, the
Pourquoi-Pas from France, and sundry British, American and Australian enterprises). This intensive exploration of the great depths and distant lands has extended
zoological knowledge considerably, not only about
adult forms but also about animals in the larval state.
Thus Denmark has organized voyages, under the
leadership of J. Schmidt, which have solved the age-
old mystery about the life cycle of the eel. An enormous
amount of invaluable material was brought home and
is still being studied today.

The study of coastal faunas has been no less fruitful. Some work was carried out on this subject in the
eighteenth century; Réaumur in particular had
achieved some interesting results, and Peyssonez had
established the animal nature of coral as long ago as
1723. This branch of zoology received serious attention
again after 1830 by H. Milne Edwards working on the
coasts of France. Numerous zoologists followed suit
along the shores of European and Mediterranean
countries; the names of H. de Lacaze-Duthiers and of

the Neapolitan Delle Chiaje are noteworthy in this context. As a result of the work of these and others, zoological research stations were established in many countries, such as France after 1860 (Roscoff, Concarneau, Wimereux, Banyuls, Algiers, etc.), England (Plymouth), Germany (Heligoland), Italy (Naples, organized by the German Dohrn, who was particularly influential, and Messina), Sweden, Norway (Bergen), the United States (Woods Hole, San Diego, Seattle, etc.), India, Japan, etc. Almost every country now has its marine zoological stations, and the research conducted in them has not only contributed enormously to our systematic knowledge about marine animals, but also to all the problems of general biology that arise from the development and reproduction of these animals. Marine biology is essentially a nineteenth-century science; marine life, being much more varied than terrestrial life and offering vast possibilities, particularly in embryogeny, has proved an enormously precious and suggestive field of study, which has already raised and solved many great biological problems. The potential of these researches is still far from being exhausted.

The political and colonial expansion of the European powers had an equally favorable influence on zoology and botany. Napoleon's expedition to Egypt in 1798 was the occasion for an intensified scientific study of that country in which zoologists like Saint-Hilaire and J. C. Savigny participated. The campaign in Morea in 1828 followed the same tradition, and, later on, Algeria and Tunisia furnished material for research. The Dutch East Indies, the Malay Archipelago and India all attracted many zoologists and botanists, who added fascinating volumes to scientific literature. In 1888—89, the Dutch expedition of the *Siboga,* organized by Max Weber, was signally successful. French Indochina was, in its turn, the scene of important botanical and zoological explorations. In Java, Treub set up the great botanical garden of Buitenzorg, which attracted many eminent botanists and zoologists. Likewise each part of tropical Africa now has its laboratories and zoological and botanical gardens. The problems relating to public health in these countries have been the source of innumerable and important biological researches and publications. The construction of the Panama Canal and the creation of the artificial lake of Gatun resulted in the setting up, on an island in the lake, of the biological station of Barro-Colorado, which is uniquely placed for the study of tropical terrestrial biology. Since the nineteenth century the whole earth has become a vast field for zoological and botanical studies, and the horizons of these studies have widened immeasurably. Newly emerging countries, notably Japan, have rapidly established themselves as active scientific centers.

PALEONTOLOGY

Paleontology is the study of flora and fauna as they existed in bygone ages on this planet. In the nineteenth century this infant science began to make invaluable and enlightening contributions to the zoology and botany of modern forms of life.

Fossils may be found abundantly in certain geological deposits and have been commented upon since antiquity. However, only a few scholars had appreciated their real value—notably, Herodotus and Strabo among the ancients; during the Renaissance, Bernard Palissy, Fracastor and Leonardo da Vinci; in the seventeenth century, Steno and Leibnitz; in the eighteenth, Réaumur, Buffon and a few of their contemporaries. The first precise studies on the subject of fossils date from this last period, but not until the nineteenth century can paleontology be regarded as a fully constituted science. Its creators as such are Cuvier, Saint-Hilaire and Lamarck for animals, and Brogniart for plants. Cuvier concentrated on fossil reptiles as well as mammals from the Paris region. His insight enabled him to interpret these remains and classify them in the existing zoological system. His paleontological writings, collected together in his *Mémoires sur les ossements fossiles* (the introduction of which is the *Discours sur les Révolutions du Globe* already mentioned) is the first work of importance on paleontology. It had three editions from 1812 to 1826 and set in motion a wave of research that has been gathering momentum ever since. Saint-Hilaire's main interest was fossilized reptile remains, while Lamarck was concerned with invertebrates (molluscs and bivalves) and published his findings in *Histoire naturelle des Animaux Sans Vertèbres* (1815—1822). Adolphe Brogniart, the son of Cuvier's co-worker Alexandre Brogniart, wrote *Histoire des végétaux fossiles* (1828), thus establishing the general framework of plant paleontology. This last paragraph indicates clearly how much paleontology owes, in its origins, to French scientists.

Paleontology is a science that has, basically, a two-fold application; first, it delves into the zoology and botany of the past and provides indispensable clues for interpreting existing organisms; second, when combined with a study of the arrangement of sediments (stratigraphy), it enables the geologist to establish a yardstick for dating the strata that contain the fossils. A particular flora and fauna corresponds to each geological era, so that deposits of different composition and situated countries or even continents apart may be safely regarded as synchronous if their fossil remains are the same. Indeed, the development of paleontology has been parallel to that of geology. It has been in existence for little more than a century, but has already produced many famous scholars. For vertebrate paleontology the most eminent workers are, in France, Gaudry, Depéret and Boule; in the United States, Cope, Marsh, Leidy, Osborn and Scott; in England, Owen and Thomas Huxley; in Russia, Kowalewsky; and in Belgium, Dollo, who studied fossils from the standpoint of what had been the way of life of the original living matter, and thus constituted a new science, *paleobiology,* the most brilliant exponent of which is O. Abel. Notable specialists in invertebrate paleontology are legion; among the leading Frenchmen are Orbigny, Barrande, Munier-Chalmas and Douville. And the great French initiators in plant paleontology include Renault, Grand'Eury, Saporta, Zeiller, etc.

Unfortunately the present-day abundance of paleontological writings can reveal no more than a minute fraction of all the forms that lived in former ages. Only in very exceptional circumstances does an organism become fossilized, even if it contains some mineral elements that are readily preserved. A creature is even more unlikely to survive as a fossil if it has no outer shell or internal skeleton. Sometimes, however, thanks to special conditions prevailing in sedimentary deposits, we chance upon delicate organisms or parts of organisms in a remarkable state of preservation. With today's technical resources it is possible to study the structure of these finds almost as thoroughly as that of living organisms. These sediments give us access to forms that may have lived as long as a billion years ago, and yet we are by no means in sight of the origins of life on this globe: we can merely perceive a biological world that was already very old. Through the fossils we can trace a succession of epochs of varying length, each with its own flora and fauna and each linked to the next by transitional forms that bring us gradually up to the world of today. But the major divisions of the animal kingdom already existed in the most distant geological eras, and were separated from each other then by similar discontinuities to those that can be observed in our time. The number of true intermediary forms (like the Jurassic bird-reptile Archaeopterix) is extremely low. On the one hand, there still exist forms that practically have not changed at all since the earliest times, e.g. Nautilus, found in Silurian deposits, which represents a peak of invertebrate development in the cephalopod molluscs; Lingula, a bivalve; and scorpions. Some groups became differentiated comparatively recently, like the mammals in Tertiary times, although it must be admitted that their previous history remains an almost totally closed book. The origins of the plant kingdom are also little known, but they seem to have developed on the whole later still; nevertheless some vascular cryptogams are already well characterized at the beginning of the Primary era. Toward the end of this same period we can discern the transition of these plants into the phanerogams (together with the ferns), and the angiosperms, so predominant today, scarcely appear at all before the late Jurassic or early Cretaceous.

It is generally true, however, that most animal and plant types descend from a very distant past. They are already well advanced when we find them and they cannot be proved to undergo any fundamental transformations. One of the most striking features in the present-day framework of the major groups is the considerable number of phyla, classes, orders and families that have completely disappeared after being of considerable importance in their time: e.g. various echinoderms of the Primary period (blastoids and cystidae), ammonites and belemnites of the Secondary, as well as a whole series of spectacular and powerful reptiles.

Likewise, in the plant kingdom, we need only think of the abundant arborescent vascular cryptogams of the Carboniferous, or of the importance of fossil Cycadaceae and Ginkgoaceae at the beginning of the Secondary alongside their present-day reduced status. However fragmentary the paleontological evidence may be, compared with what actually existed, it has considerably enlarged our general knowledge about life on earth, and we may confidently expect many more such enlightening finds in the future.

THE BASIC CONSTITUTION OF ORGANISMS:

CELLULAR THEORY AND CYTOLOGY

Another major milestone in biology was reached in the nineteenth century with the development of the cellular theory. The fundamental notion of the *cell* revealed the structural unity of all organisms, both animal and vegetable, and was a vital acquisition for the understanding of life.

Until then, scarcely anyone had considered the organism other than as a whole. Only a few rare pioneers had attempted to ascertain the elements of an organism. Leeuwenhoek, for example, in his microscopic investigations, had perceived the blood globules; within the globules of amphibians he had even glimpsed a vesicular formation, the nucleus, without understanding the full significance of his discovery. He had also seen muscular fibers (cf. Fig. 2). Even before this, in 1667, Hooke, who was a physicist rather than a naturalist, had made some very fine sections of cork and discovered that it was formed by an agglomeration of tiny cavities separated by walls and arranged like the compartments in a honeycomb; he had named these compartments *cells* and illustrated them. In 1675 Malpighi made very accurate drawings, not only of cells but also of various plant tissues (inner bark, wood, growing layers).[1] Figure 6 (cf. also the drawing of the *Lemna* root, Fig. 2) shows that this structural detail was also perceived by Leeuwenhoek. Indeed it is surprising that the study of vegetable tissues was not followed up immediately. No more progress was made until the early nineteenth century, when the French botanist Mirbel turned his attention to the formation of liverworts and eventually discovered the nuclei within the cell (1831). In 1808 Treviranus, and a few years later Meyen, working in Germany, as well as the Frenchmen Dutrochet and Turpin, also resumed the study of cell formation and established the idea that all plants were associations of cells. Dutrochet even extended this conception to animals, and in 1826 Turpin published a paper with the lengthy but significant title *Observations on the origin and basic formation of cellular tissue, on each of the vesicles of this tissue considered as a distinct individuality with its own vital center of growth and propagation, each individual vesicle being considered as destined to form, by*

[1] *Anatome plantarum, cui subjungitur appendix iteratus et auctus ejusdem authoris de ovo incubato observationes continens* (London, 1675). Plates 1 to 7 in the appendix are a very accurate representation of the development of the chicken.

agglomeration, the compound individuality of all plants whose structural organization includes more than one vesicle. This is essentially a summary of the whole cellular theory. In 1831 the English botanist Robert Brown examined the cells in the staminal hairs of *Tradescantia* flowers and in the epidermis of orchids and discovered in them the *regular* and constant presence of a differentiated spherical body, which he called the *nucleus* of the cell.

At about this time, the compound microscope was

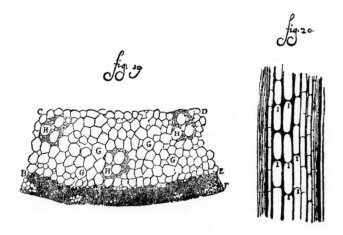

Fig. 6. Plant cellular structures drawn by Leeuwenhoek (letter 29, 1679). *fig. 19*, part of tranverse section of a grass stem (*cujusdam straminis in transversum discissae*); *BEF*, cortex; *G*, vessels; *H*, other vessels mixed up with previous kind (*undiquaeque replete exiguis vasculis; in haec vasa liquorem [tempore quo stramen incrementum solet capere] rapidissime vidi influentem*, etc. *fig. 20, G* elements of *fig. 19* seen in longitudinal section (*IIII est valvalarum locus, ibique vasa sunt omnium augustissima*).

developing rapidly, and achromatic combinations were achieved for the lenses, like those that had been in use since 1757 in astronomical instruments. This made it possible to increase the enlarging power up to 400 or 500 diameters so that the structure of the organs could now be studied under satisfactory conditions.

Furthermore, Bichat (1771—1802), whose life was so regrettably short, had laid the foundations of a new science, which was later to be known as animal histology. Shortly before his death (1801) he published his *Anatomie générale appliquée à la physiologie et à la médecine,* in which he proved that the various elements of the organs are made up of tissues. Working on human corpses, he used various methods to separate these elements, such as desiccation, maceration, coction, application of acids and alkalis, etc. "Chemistry," he wrote, "has its simple bodies... anatomy has its simple tissues, which, by their combinations, make up the organs." Death prevented him from arriving at the element common to all these tissues and stopped him at the very threshold of that new science, *general anatomy.*

In 1824 Prévost and Dumas picked up the threads of Spallanzani's experiments and succeeded in fertilizing a frog's egg and in observing its progressive *fragmentation* (this process is today called *segmentation*) into a series of spheres, the precise significance of which escaped them. These spheres were, of course, individual cells. In 1825 Purkinje examined the egg from a hen's ovary and described a transparent sphere that he found in it, giving the name *germinative* vesicle to what is in reality the nucleus. Finally, in 1827, guided by the findings of Prévost and Dumas, which had been published shortly before, in 1825, K. von Baer was able to distinguish the real mammalian egg in the Graafian follicles from the ovary of a bitch.[2] Nine years later Coste isolated Purkinje's vesicle—the nucleus, in other words—within the egg.

One of the first scientists to take advantage of the recently perfected microscope was Félix Dujardin, who is known as one of the founders of protozoology. In 1835 he studied a foraminifer and the amoeba, and gave the expressive name *sarcode* to the living substance of which these simple creatures are made. The term *sarcode* has been dropped for the less felicitous *protoplasm*, which was suggested in 1846 by the botanist H. von Mohl. He described it thus: "A glutinous substance, insoluble in water, contracting into globulous masses, sticking to dissection needles and capable of being stretched like mucus. In lower animals it is found interposed with other structural elements."

[2]In his famous letter to the St. Petersburg Academy of Science, in which he announces his discovery (1827), Baer is still influenced by the idea that the Graafian vesicle is in fact the egg. In his conclusions he considers it to be the *maternal* egg that contains the *fetal* egg. "Mammals have, therefore, an egg within an egg, or, if I may use the expression, an egg raised to the power of two." This confusion indicates how heavy was the weight of accepted ideas. In 1834 Coste finally rejected this strange conception and identified once and for all what is properly speaking the egg. He also isolated the elements that make a cell of the egg: membrane, granulous mass (vitellus) and Purkinje's vesicle (nucleus).

These two series of studies, on animals and plants respectively, had gradually revealed the elements of the cell. Cellular theory was formulated rather dogmatically by the German botanist Schleiden in 1836: "The cell is a minute organism. Every plant, even the most highly developed, is an aggregate of cells, all completely individualized and having an existence of their own." This notion was extended to animals by the anatomist Schwann in 1839. Several authorities (Valentin, Müller, Henle) had just perceived a cellular structure, similar to that described by botanists, in epithelia, glands, spinal cord, etc.

Schleiden and Schwann attributed excessive importance to the membrane, and they introduced some erroneous ideas about the formation of cells. In fact, they conceived it as a kind of crystallization within a mother substance, the cytoblastema, around granules that are centers of cell concentration and that produce vesicles. The initial granule was, for them, the nucleole, the vesicle when formed was the nucleus; the new cell was not really formed until the eventual differentiation of the membrane. These ideas were accepted until after 1870, but in spite of them in 1854 Max Schultze defined a cell as "a small mass of protoplasm containing a nucleus," and in 1855 Virchow came forth with the aphorism *Omnis cellula e cellula*, "Every cell originates from a previous cell."

On the basis of the various formulae just mentioned, there was a spate of observations that strove to apply this theory of cellular structure to the makeup of all manner of organs and tissues. Histology developed very rapidly thanks to the creation and perfecting of special coloration techniques that, after the application of appropriate reagents, selected only the nucleus or other parts of the cell, and of techniques whereby different tissues could be disassociated from each other, the cellular membrane could be impregnated with gold and silver salts, etc. A particularly useful method was worked out whereby the tissues could be placed in some very homogeneous solid medium (paraffin wax, celloidin) and cut up into a series of sections, each only some thousands of a millimeter thick, by means of highly perfected microtomes. These techniques made it feasible to study any question concerning structure on a cellular scale. Among the many pioneers in histology the name of Kölliker is noteworthy, as is that of Ranvier, who may be considered the creator of histophysiology because of his insistence that function and structure are inseparable.

Space does not allow us to detail the achievements of histology. The constitution of all tissues was deciphered and analyzed. Notable results were obtained on the most specialized tissues, like muscular tissue and nervous tissue and their mutual connections. Nervous tissue is the most complex of all and decisive progress in this domain was due to special techniques developed and applied by Ranvier, Weigert, Nissl, Retzius, Apathy, Golgi and especially Ramon y Cajal, who finally established the individuality and the connections of the nervous cells, or *neurones,* as they were termed by Waldeyer. Every tissue and organ without exception throughout the two kingdoms is today known to be of cellular structure. It is at the base of every function of each organism. Modern biology is in fact synonymous with cellular biology.

The formation of new cells is one of the most important aspects of cellular theory. Schleiden and Schwann went completely astray on this point. Cells derive from one another by *division,* but this dividing process was not fully analyzed until after 1870. In exceptional cases division is simply the result of the simultaneous stretching and narrowing of the cellular body and the nucleus; this is known as *direct* division. But division is usually *indirect:* this is a much more complex process and has been termed *mitosis* or *karyokinesis.*[3] Indirect division is triggered by fundamental changes in the nucleus, which seems initially to disappear; then the membrane becomes absorbed and its contents break up into a certain number of bodies. This number, which is constant in all the tissues of each species, we shall call 2n. These bodies, the chromosomes, assume the basic colorations. These chromosomes are units that do not become apparent until the moment of division, but it is assumed for numerous reasons that they are invariably present, even when invisible. At the time of division each chromosome splits lengthwise in two, and the newly formed halves move

[3]Karyokinesis is the generally accepted term today; it was coined by W. Schleicher *(Arch. f. mikr. Anat.,* Vol. XVI [1879], p. 262).

in opposite directions toward the two poles of a barrel-shaped structure made up of very fine filaments. On arriving at the poles, each of these two groups of 2n male chromosomes become reconstituted into a new nucleus, while at the same time the mother cell divides through the middle into two daughter cells. Virchow's aphorism might therefore be rephrased *omnis nucleus e nucleo*. This complicated process was gradually analyzed and generalized between 1870 and 1880 thanks, largely, to careful study of the fertilization of the egg. The honor of describing and understanding the whole process goes to two German biologists, the botanist E. Strasburger and the anatomist W. Flemming. Strasburger in particular was the first to follow *in vivo* each successive step in the cells on the staminal hairs of *Tradescantia*; the same study of the living process has been achieved on many animal eggs, on epithelial cells, and on the white globules of amphibians; the whole process has recently been filmed. We shall return later to these phenomena when considering their fundamental importance in the study of growth and heredity. The works published since 1880 on karyokinesis in plants and animals are almost innumerable.[4]

It can thus be seen that, in the final analysis, all biological problems must be considered on the cellular

[4]Detailed analyses of karyokinesis have been made by L. F. Henneguy, *Leçons sur la cellule* (Paris, 1896) and by E. B. Wilson, *The Cell in Development and Inheritance* (3d ed.; New York, 1925).

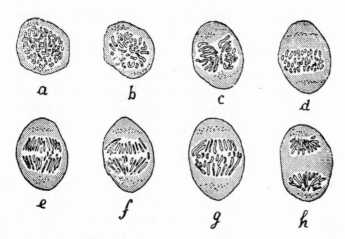

Fig. 7. Successive stages of karyokinesis followed *in vivo* on an epithelial cell from a tadpole's tail. *a*, half an hour after beginning; *b*, 1-1/2 hours; *c*, 2 hours; *d*, 2-3/4 hours; *e-g*, 3 hours; *h*, 3 hours 5 minutes (Flemming, 1879, *Arch f. mikr. Anat*, Vol. XIX).

scale. There is a cellular substratum to every function. It is the cell that assimilates, breathes and eliminates. It accomplishes the synthesis and breaking down of substances, either by direct action or through agents that it produces. The study of the life of the cell, cytology, has become a science in its own right and is receiving much attention today as one of the most fundamental aspects of present-day biology. Whole laboratories, textbooks[5] and specialized periodicals are now devoted to covering the vast development cytology has undergone.

[5]For example, A. Guilliermond, G. Mangenot and L. Plantefol, *Traité de Gytologie végétale* (Paris, 1933).

Cytology has expanded and continues to expand mainly on observation, but more recently it has also become an experimental science. Many cellular processes are analyzed these days that have been modified by a variety of interventions. A significant example is the success of the experiment to cultivate *in vitro* the cells of higher organisms and to make them go on multiplying indefinitely. The initial experiment with this objective was the brain child of an American biologist, R. G. Harrison, who worked on the nerve cells of newt embryos. The actual culture was first achieved from chicken embryos and was the work of Alexis Carrel. The tissues cultivated in this way become practically immortal. Carrel succeeded in making the process continue for more than twenty years, far beyond the life expectancy of a chicken, and yet the strength and capacity of the elements to multiply was by no means diminished. This example indicates clearly the exceptionally important potential of the study of cells.

FERTILIZATION AND THE EGG

One of the most important chapters in the story of cytology concerns the egg and its fertilization. In its general outlines this chapter presents a unified picture for both plant and animal kingdoms and it has constituted a positive basis for the study of the problem of heredity. This, too, then, must be reckoned a major milestone in biology, covering the period 1870 to the present.

We have already referred to the almost prophetic

inscription *Ex ovo omnia* in Harvey's frontispiece to
Exercitationes de generatione animalium (1651). This
aphorism did not assume its full significance until the
advent of the cellular theory. The egg, which is in fact
the initial stage of every being, is one cell, as Coste was
to formulate explicitly in 1847.[6] But it is no ordinary
cell, in that it results from the fusion, through fertilization, of two elements each of which has the value of
a cell. These are the two *gametes*, the female gamete or
oöcyte (*oösphere* in plants) and the male gamete or
spermatozoid (*antherozoid* in plants). Fertilization
results from the penetration of the female gamete by
the male gamete. Reference has already been made to
Leeuwenhoek's discovery of spermatozoa in 1677 and to
the arguments that raged for more than a century on
the subject. The actual penetration by the male gamete
into the female was not observed under the microscope
until the latter half of the nineteenth century. The
French botanist Thuret was the first to observe this
phenomenon in a plant, the *Fucus* or common bladder-
wrack of European coasts (1854). The first zoologist was
the Swiss Hermann Fol, who witnessed the penetration

[6]Victor Coste, *Histoire générale et particulière du développe-
ment des êtres organisés.* "Modern science has adopted the old
adage *omne vivum ex ovo* as if it were proved by demonstration
since the discovery of the analogy existing between the egg of
man, of mammals and of oviparous animals. What the great
Harvey could only express as a bold stroke of foresight or as a
premature generalization, we are able now to state as the irrefutable result of our experiments and dissections; everything that
lives develops from a cell or from an egg."

in a starfish egg. Immediately after the entry of the male gamete, the egg, previously uncovered, becomes surrounded by a membrane and development begins. Growth consists of a series of cellular divisions that isolate successively 2, 4, 8, 16, 32, 64, 128, etc., cells, in the shape of little spheres. This had been observed in a frog's egg by Prévost and Dumas (1824), but at that time the cellular significance was not understood. These cells are at first identical in shape although progressively smaller in size, but eventually groups of them become differentiated as the outlines of the embryo's organs take shape. The process assumes a

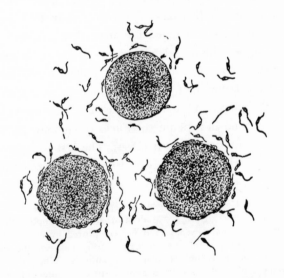

Fig. 8. Fertilization in *Fucus vesiculosus*. Three oöspheres with antherozoids swarming around them. (Thuret, 1854, *Ann. Sci. not., Botan.*, series 4, Vol II.)

variety of forms, depending especially on the size of the egg and the supply of reserve substances (vitellus) that are contained in it.

The fertilization and development of the egg have now been studied and followed in detail in an enormous number of animals and plants from every group, from mammals to lower invertebrates, from the higher plants to the mosses and thallophytes (algae and fungi). Only one spermatozoid penetrates the egg (n onospermic fertilization). The fertilized egg at once acquires an immunity against any further fertilization even when the newly formed membrane is removed.

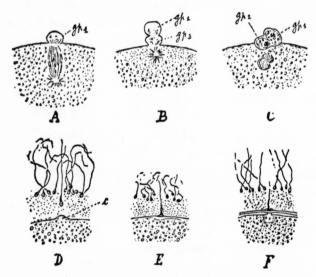

Fig. 9. Discharge of polar bodies (*ABC*). First observation in *vivo* (*DEF*) of the penetration of the egg by the spermatozoid in a starfish (*Asterias glacialis*) (Fol, 1879, *Arch. Sci. Phys. Nat. Geneva*, Vol. LVIII.)

The initial unicellular state of the individual, whether animal or plant, is one of the greatest revelations to be made by biology. No less significant is the study of the formation of the oöcytes and spermatozoids inside the glands that produce them (gonads: testicles in the male, ovaries in the female). Likewise here, the processes, although apparently so varied, conform to a unified pattern, one especially important aspect of which must be mentioned.

The gametes are the final result of the multiplication, through a long series of cellular divisions, of the germinal cells that constitute the ovary and the testicle; the spermatozoids, in particular, are produced in enormous numbers. As already stated, when division takes place, 2n chromosomes (the number is constant for each species) become visible. The last two cellular divisions result in the formation of *mature* gametes: the spermatozoids and the oöcyte. When the latter has expelled, one after the other, by two cellular divisions, two little corpuscles (the polar bodies), the number of chromosomes is reduced by half, from 2n to n. This takes place by virtue of a special mechanism that is uniform and general in this double terminal division of cells. The *diploid* cellular state (2n chromosomes) therefore gives way, in the gametes, to a *haploid* state (n chromosomes); this process is known as *chromatic reduction*, or meiosis. At fertilization, the spermatozoid merges with the oöcyte and the nuclei of the two gametes fuse, adding their respective chromosomes together (n + n = 2n) so that the diploid state is recon-

stituted in the fertilized egg. Thus fertilization is preceded by meiosis for each gamete and may therefore be
regarded as a general process that insures that the
chromosomes are constant in number throughout successive generations. This precise mechanism applies
throughout both kingdoms and its significance from the
point of view of heredity hardly needs to be stressed.
From 1875 this process was brought to light con-
currently with studies of karyokinesis. A whole series of
works was devoted to the subject, notably those of
Strasburger and L. Guignard on plants and of
A. Schneider, O. Bütschli, O. and R. Hertwig and
E. van Beneden on animals. The contribution of the
last named, a Belgian zoologist, is particularly noteworthy. In 1883 he succinctly described the chromosomic mechanism of fertilization in a threadworm,
Ascaris megalocephala, which is parasitic in the horse's
intestine. The facts were further elaborated by
T. Boveri, likewise working on the threadworm, in
1887, since which date animals and plants of all classes
have received similar attention. Meiosis itself was
finally and completely analyzed in 1910 when the
Belgian botanist Grégoire made his perfectly clear
and general account of the subject.

It should be noted, in passing, that the fertilization
of the egg is not an infallible rule. In quite a number
of animals and plants the unfertilized female gamete or
oöcyte may develop with some modifications and in a
variety of circumstances. This phenomenon, known as
parthenogenesis, was first reported in plant lice by

Bonnet in 1740. But in this case various pieces of compensatory mechanism intervene, which make up for meiosis in the absence of fertilization. Since 1900 it has been possible to achieve parthenogenesis experimentally on eggs, which normally require fertilization. Experimental parthenogenesis was first discovered by J. Loeb and subsequently successfully applied (by various processes) to a wide variety of animals. Among the outstanding authors of works in this connection, mention should be made of the Frenchmen Yves Delage and E. Bataillon. The latter achieved experimental parthenogenesis in a frog (1910) simply by pricking the virgin egg, and, more recently, an American biologist, Pincus, obtained the same result on a rabbit.

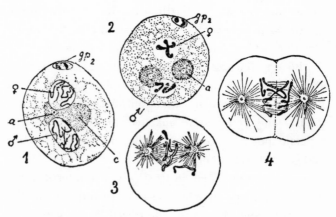

Fig. 10. Paternal and maternal chromosomes in the fertilized egg of *Ascaris megalocephala* (E. Van Beneden, 1883, Boveri, 1887.)

UNICELLULAR ORGANIMUS AND PROTISTOLOGY

An organism is, therefore, a complex edifice of innumerable cells differentiated according to the tissues making up the various organs. But some organisms may consist of one single cell and there are a great many species, both animal and vegetable, that are *unicellular*. In the animal kingdom they form the varied sub-kingdom of the Protozoa, and, among the plants, many algae are also unicellular. The dividing line between animal and plant is so difficult to draw at this level that some biologists contend that these lower organisms should be classified together in a third kingdom, the *Protista*. Precise knowledge of these forms only goes back to the nineteenth century, but Leeuwenhoek had already seen and described quite a number of them, especially Infusoria and Amoebas. From 1830 on, Dujardin was one of the very first to describe them precisely and, as we saw previously, it was his work on a fresh-water foraminifer that led him to suggest the term *sarcode* to designate the cellular substance. He had understood clearly the simplicity of organization in these lower creatures, unlike his contemporary, the German micographer Ehrenberg. The latter left behind him much important and admirably documented work, but he mistakenly attributed to the Protista, particularly the Infusoria, a complicated structure that is simply nonexistent.

The Protozoa received much attention in the second half of the nineteenth century. It was ascertained that the various types were extremely diversified in spite of their common unicellularity. It was also discovered what complicated transformations are undergone by some of these simple creatures when in process of multiplication. Indeed, many present an evolutive cycle that has multiple and complex phases; their sexuality processes, for example, have some very special characters, both in the manner and the circumstances of their production. Furthermore, a considerable number of Protozoa are parasites and swarm in the organs that they infest to the extent of being dreaded pathogenic agents and the cause of serious disease and epidemics. This is true of the dysentery amoeba and of many forms of the Sporozoa, among them the genus *Plasmodium*; the latter is the agent of malaria, a disease that, during the course of history, has transformed populated regions into veritable deserts and that constituted one of the most serious obstacles to European settlement in Africa in the nineteenth century. The propagation of these parasitic forms has proved doubly difficult to decipher because, in many cases, their evolutive cycle entails their passing alternately through two totally different hosts; the mosquito and man, for example, in the case of the malarial *Plasmodium*. In this particular instance, it was the French doctor A. Laveran who discovered *Plasmodium* in human blood as the agent of the "marsh disease" and the English doctor R. Ross who proved that it also passesthroughthemosquito, which injects it into man. The study of the evolutive cycle of parasitic Protozoa has been of immense practical, as well as academic, value since the late nineteenth century.

Because of their unicellular structure, the Protista offer specially favorable conditions for the study of cellular physiology and, in particular, of problems concerning nutrition and elementary metabolism. Much fruitful research is being conducted on these subjects at the present time.

Generally speaking, the study of Protozoa has developed to the extent that we can speak of *Protistology* as a separate science that deals with a very special, indeed a fundamental, aspect of life.

THE SIMPLEST FORMS OF LIFE;

BACTERIOLOGY; FILTERABLE VIRUSES

E. Haeckel, whose bold and sometimes unrealistic deductions about evolution will be discussed later, asserted that the simplest forms of Protista were the *Monera*, mere masses of protoplasm without a differentiated nucleus; but a well-constituted nucleus has now been found in all the Protozoa and the Monera are only a myth. However, the same question arose again, in connection with bacteria; these make up a considerable group of organisms allied to the algae, and have no individualized nucleus. Much research has been done with a view to discovering a nucleus or its equivalent in these bacteria, but the problem has still not been finally solved. However, even if there is no individualized nucleus in bacteria comparable to that in the cells of all other organisms, at least it has been possible by means of appropriate dyes to distinguish certain granulations in some. These are normally scattered about inside their cytoplasm, but, at the time of spore formation, they become concentrated in more or less distinct groups. The fact that these granulations can be differentially color-dyed seems to suggest that they constitute the bacterial equivalent of the substance that forms the chromosomes of normal cells, and, consequently, they may be said to represent a *diffused nucleus.*

Whatever the real significance of this assimilation, the fact remains that bacteria represent a special state of living matter, morphologically simpler than the cell proper and, therefore, a lower form of life than the cell.

These organisms are the smallest in existence but their size ranges over a vast scale, from rod bacteria several thousandths of a millimeter in length down to others that are too small to be seen by any microscope, even the latest electronic model. There are, therefore, *invisible* organisms, some of which reveal their presence by their disease-producing properties and constitute well-defined viruses. The discovery of these incredibly small organisms has extended considerably the domain of life. Though invisible, these creatures can be measured by their ability to pass through filters having pores of a size that can be estimated. They may be equal in size to molecules, and they present many entirely new problems concerning the organization of living matter. In the case of contagious plant diseases, like the tobacco-plant disease, the American biologist

W. M. Stanley was able to isolate these viruses in a *crystallized state* (1936). The study of these *ferment viruses* (to which are allied the substances called, by Hérelle, *bacteriophages*) is one of the most recent and important problems confronting science today. Their existence carries the lower limits of life back beyond the cellular constitution to a scale that can only be defined as molecular.

THE DEVELOPMENT OF THE ORGANISM;
NATURAL AND EXPERIMENTAL EMBRYOLOGY;
TERATOLOGY

After our brief glimpse of life in its minutest and simplest form, we now return to the cellular domain to consider another recent branch of biology, namely embryology. Although its very nature prevents it from being a truly autonomous science, embryology is none-theless one of the most fruitful of present-day biological disciplines.

Embryology rests basically on cellular theory: the egg, which is the initial stage of organisms, is a cell and the development of the embryo can be summarized as a succession of cellular divisions. Furthermore, trans-formist theories (cf. Chapter 4) have been of major importance in the study of embryology, which was one of the most intensely worked branches of biology in the late nineteenth century. Thanks to the techniques of microscopic anatomy and, in particular, to the micro-tome, embryology has developed rapidly and exten-sively. It has been possible, for example, to follow, cell by cell, the formation and the differentiation of the embryo, both from the point of view of the whole organism and from that of each individual organ. Comparative studies of embryos from all groups of animals have also yielded rich results.

The development of every species depends on a mechanism that is regulated with extreme precision. The cell lineage of all the organs has been established; this lineage is almost absolutely uniform within the major groups of animals. Comparison of results has made it possible to measure with remarkable precision the natural affinities of these groups and thereby to provide a firm basis for classification. At the beginning of the nineteenth century, K. von Baer had already foreseen this fact, and, in spite of the scanty information at his disposal, he had transposed Cuvier's classification onto the embryogenic plane.

The subsequent development of embryogeny more than justified the conception of epigenesis, just as C. F. Wolff had formulated it in 1759. Nevertheless in the late nineteenth century a controversy arose, comparable to the one about preformation and epigenesis. The question was: do the various stages and differentiations in development represent a succession of steps irrevocably determined from the beginning and *inscribed, in some way, within the structure of the egg?* Or is this succession to some extent dependent on the extrinsic conditions in which the embryo and its sundry parts happen to find themselves during the course of development? An eminent German anatomist, W. His, had imagined the egg as a *mosaic* of parts, each of which represented in advance some definite part of the future embryo; in his view the egg was *anisotropic*. This opposed the conception of the *isotropy* of the egg and of the equivalence of all its parts. Thus the old quarrel about preformation and epigenesis was fought again over the terrain of cellular biology.

Under normal conditions, everything does in fact happen according to a definite succession, as if there were a strict predetermination. On the other hand, the eggs of certain species are obviously anisotropic. Direct observation has established beyond any possible doubt that some of the first outlines discernible in the embryo, and subsequently the organs that derive from them, originate from cells that themselves derive from some definite part or other of the egg. In order to settle this question, it was necessary to experiment on the egg and on the initial stages of its development. *Experimental embryology* came into existence as a result, its founders being L. Chabry (1855—1893) in France and W. Roux (1850—1924) in Germany. By means of a variety of ingenious technical processes, it was possible to remove a part of the substance of the egg, or to kill or displace one or another of the first cells formed, thereby creating new conditions for development. As early as 1887 Chabry had invented a *micromanipulator* for this purpose. Since then more ingenious ones have been devised, the most accomplished, at the present time, being the brain child of M. de Fonbrune. This apparatus enables the operator to make *micromovements* in any direction while working on the maximum enlargements of the microscope.[7] This and other techniques, in skilled hands, have enabled experimental embryology to pose and solve a whole series of very important problems, which we have not the space to detail here. The works of H. Spemann in Germany and S. Horstadius in Sweden are worth a special mention. The former conducted his experiments on amphibians (newts) and transplanted a determined portion of the anterior lip of the gastrula-stage blastospore onto the side of an embryo. At the place of the graft, he effected the differentiation of an additional embryo upon the normal one. The grafted portion plays the part of an *organizer* and seems to determine a new personality. By various means Horstadius succeeded (in particular on sea urchins) in combining parts of embryos into one composite embryo.

The experimental analysis of results such as these is of the highest significance, and, referring back to the question raised earlier, it transpires from all the observations and experiments made so far that, in fact, if not in principle, the development of the embryo is preordained in detail and prepared for by the heterogeneity of the *fertilized* egg (the act of fertilization brings about important readjustments in the structure of the oöcyte). The particular circumstances in which development takes place may permit or inhibit this

[7]These movements are controlled by an apparatus that corresponds, on the microscopic scale, to the joy-stick used in steering aircraft.

development, but they do not, in any real sense, direct it. The determining factor is something intrinsic, but this does not imply any metaphysical or teleological predestination. These few examples will suffice to indicate what fundamentally important problems are being examined these days by embryogenic research work.

However well regulated nature may be, strange anomalies and aberrations sometimes occur in embryogeny. These are due to extrinsic conditions and they result in freaks, the study of which constitutes *teratology*. Men have long been impressed and puzzled by freak animals and humans, but scientific teratology hardly existed before E. Geoffroy Saint-Hilaire, whose work was continued by his son Isidore. The insight of the former into the determinism of the production of freaks was quite remarkable, and the application of experimental methods has confirmed his theories. The experimental production of freaks, or *teratogeny*, was developed during the nineteenth century, notably by C. Dareste (1822—1899) on the chicken embryo. Today, the various techniques of experimental embryology make it possible to obtain all kinds of instructive freaks from a variety of animals (especially birds, amphibians and echinoderms).

Physiology

The living organism is made up of a whole set of functional systems. Morphology analyzes the structure of these systems; physiology studies their functions and requires the knowledge of the essential mechanism of the various metabolic processes that the living organism performs. It goes without saying that physiology could not develop on a firm basis until the nineteenth century, by which time chemistry and physics had made sufficient progress.

Before this basis was established, ignorance of physiology was covered up by a priori conceptions, most of which were merely a form of words. The obvious differences between inert and living bodies were attributed by the ancients to a special principle, *the breath of life* (pneuma), which animates the matter within the organism. This concept, known as animism, prevailed until the seventeenth century. Even Descartes allowed that the soul was something immaterial and outside the province of his mechanistic philosophy; with this proviso, he built up a physiology in which everything is reduced to matter and mobility. The details of his system appear crude by our standards, as indeed they did to Descartes' contemporary, Pascal. Nevertheless these conceptions contain some profound intuitions, and they inspired two schools of thought that flourished in the late seventeenth century. These were the *iatromechanistic,* developed by the Italian Borelli (1608—1670), and *iatrochemistry,* due to Sylvius (1614—1672) in Holland. Albert de Haller (1703—1777), in the eight volumes of his *Elementa physiologiae corporis humani,* made a general summary of contemporary knowledge without adding any essential new facts or ideas. In the eighteenth century, the animism of the ancients was revived with the far-fetched theories of Stahl, and it was resumed more soberly in the vitalism of the Montpellier school with Bordeu (1722—1776), Barthez (1734—1806), etc. The latter held that a special force, the *force vitale,* regulated the interplay of mechanistic forces within the organism and insured the coordination and effectiveness of these forces. All these conceptions contain little more than verbal gymnastics intended to conceal unsurmounted difficulties.

Real physiology can only derive from experiment, and men like Réaumur, Spallanzani and Lavoisier must be counted the first real physiologists. But vitalism still had its supporters throughout most of the nineteenth century; Bichat decentralized the theory to some extent by admitting, instead of one single vital force in the various tissues, two distinct categories of properties; the first being vital and essentially unstable, the second belonging to the physical world and, as such, being fixed and calculable. Bichat held the view that life itself is simply the conflict between these two types of forces and that death is the final triumph of the physical forces over the vital ones. J. Müller (1801—1858), who exercised much influence in Germany by his teaching and through his pupils (among them Helmholtz, Virchow, Du Bois-Reymond, Brücke, Schwann, Henle, Pflüger, Haeckel), remained a vitalist all his life, but he is still considered by present-day German biologists (particularly by Verworn) to be one of the greatest promoters of nineteenth-century physiology.

THE ESTABLISHMENT AND EXPANSION OF

GENERAL PHYSIOLOGY: CLAUDE BERNARD

It was in France that the reaction against vitalism made itself felt and that the first real progress was made in physiology on a firm basis of experimental methods. This great movement was primarily the work of F. Magendie (1783—1855) and especially of his disciple Claude Bernard (1813—1878). The former made experimentation the *sole* basis for physiology and rigorously applied this principle to the study of a series of physiological problems. Typical in this connection are his works on the functions of the roots of the spinal nerves, which he elucidated exhaustively, independently of the findings of C. Bell. It was a great British physiologist, A. Waller, who rendered full justice to Magendie in this matter.[8]

Claude Bernard is incontestably the greatest master of physiology in the nineteenth century. In 1913, at the occasion of the centenary of his birth, Dastre said, "He chased away the phantoms that used to encumber this science. Physiology had been the humble servant of medicine; he made an independent science of it, with its own methods and aims. He accomplished a revolution of which following generations have been unaware, because the results of it are now so well acquired and assimilated that they have become, more or less, a part of our mentality, or as Montaigne said, 'l'habitude en ôte l'étrangeté.'" Claude Bernard made numerous

[8]Cf. *Meet. Brit. Assoc. Advanc. Science* (Portsmouth, 1911).

fundamental discoveries in all aspects of physiology: functions of the digestive juices, the part played by the pancreas in the digestion of fats, discovery of the glyco-genic function of the liver and of the metabolism of sugars, the role of glucose in the production of animal heat (this completed the previous discoveries of Lavoisier), discovery and analysis of the role of the vasomotor nerves, physiology of the sympathetic nervous system, study of the mechanism of poisons (strychnine, curare, etc.), mechanism of carbon mon-oxide poisoning, conception of the "milieu intérieur" as a regulator of the various functions. All this he achieved without ever letting himself be drawn into premature generalizations or verbal illusions; all his conclusions were established on crucial experiments. He had a perfectly clear conception of general physiol-ogy as it applies to both animals and plants; this cel-lular interpretation of physiology was to receive much attention after his death. All his observations first appeared in special notes and articles before being col-lected and coordinated in a magnificent series of volumes that reproduced his lectures at the Collège de France. Failing health obliged him to rest from lec-turing in 1865; he used the extra leisure to publish a book on his ideas concerning method in physiology. This was his *Introduction à l'étude de la médecine expérimentale,* destined to be as immortal as Descartes' *Discours de la méthode.* In it he formulated for all time the basic and ineluctable rules of physiological experimentation. These enabled him to establish that all phenomena taking place within a living organism obey laws as precise and constant as any that govern inert matter. He finally expelled "force vitale" and vitalism from the domain of physiology. Experimentation became as rigorous for the physiologist as ever it was for physicist or chemist; basically, the method was first to establish a control by maintaining all conditions, other than the one being studied, equal and constant (experimental determinism). Multiple and delicate mechanisms in the organism insure a harmonious balance, which gives the illusion of a built-in finality; but, in fact, nothing indicates the existence of a special force. This summary must suffice to indicate how decisive was Claude Bernard's contribution to biology.

With Bernard, physiology became an exact and positive science, and it is interesting to note that the positivist philosophy of Auguste Comte had considerable influence over Bernard's mind. Comte was familiar with the work of Magendie and displayed shrewd insight into the conditions necessary for physiological research; as early as 1836 he had declared that the time was ripe for physiology to free itself, not only from metaphysics, but also from medicine.

Alongside Bernard, mention should be made of Flourens (1794—1867), to whom physiology is indebted for his important findings, notably about the nervous system (semicircular canals). Among Bernard's disciples were such brilliant physiologists as Paul Bert (1833—1886), A. Dastre (1844—1917), N. Gréhant (1838—1910) and A. d'Arsonval (1851—1940). Outside his immediate sphere of influence, another Frenchman, J.-P. Marey (1830—1904), became the leading light in the biological study of movement by the graphic method, which was created by the German physiologist Ludwig (1816—1895); Marey was the precursor and almost the inventor of the cinematograph, invaluable today for the accurate observation of many biological phenomena. A. Chauveau (1827—1917), a forerunner of Pasteur in the study of viruses, gave a great impetus to studies of energy consumption and production in organisms. More will be said later about Brown-Séquard (1819—1894) and his rejuvenation experiments.

Eminent contributions to nineteenth-century physiology were made in a number of countries: Germany (Ludwig, Helmoltz, Du Bois-Reymond, Brücke, Pflüger, Rübner, etc.); England (Schäfer, Sherrington, Bayliss, Starling, etc.); and Russia (Pavlov). These various physiologists borrowed their favorite methods either from the domain of chemistry or from that of physics.

It is not possible to consider here all that physiology owes to these men and their individual specializations. Electricity proved to be of great value in the study of the nervous system (Ludwig, Du Bois-Reymond, Helmholtz, Sherrington, Lapicque). Electrical instruments like the cathode ray oscillograph make it possible to follow the passage of thoughts through the brain. The calorimetric study of exchanges of energy has shed much light on problems of nutrition; the works of Atwater and Benedect, of J. Lefèvre and others reveal the high peak of perfection that this technique has reached.[9]

CHEMICAL PHYSIOLOGY: ENZYMES, VITAMINS,
HORMONES AND ENDOCRINOLOGY

Even more important than these last-mentioned techniques were those based on chemical data. The term *organic chemistry* is based on the idea, generally admitted in the nineteenth century, that a distinct and determinable chemical formula could be applied to the various compounds produced by the organism. In the early years of the nineteenth century, chemists had already extracted a considerable number of special bodies from plants (e.g. alkaloids); between 1817 and 1822 Pelletier and Caventou isolated strychnine, veratrine, brucine, quinine, etc., at about the same time Chevreul was working on the composition of animal fats. In 1828 Wöhler succeeded in producing *in vitro* the synthesis of urea. It is safe to say that, since that date, all compounds produced by living cells have been synthesized, one by one, within the framework of chemistry. This does not, of course, apply to vital actions because the organism possesses special agents for synthesizing or disintegrating, and these respond to slight changes of temperature or air pressure. In the laboratory such actions necessarily require more powerful and drastic methods.

[9]A good idea of the general state of physiology, as it was a few years ago, can be gained from *Traité élémentaire de Physiologie*, by E. Gley (Paris, Baillière).

Enzymes. Generally speaking, the agents of these transformations *in vivo* are what are today called catalysts, the most typical of which are the *enzymes.* The first to be described was the one that, in germinating barley, turned starch into sugar; it was isolated in malt by Payen and Persoz (1822), who called it diastase, but the name enzyme is now in general use for all these *soluble ferments.* All the transformations in digestion have been reduced to enzymic actions. The whole of glandular physiology can, in the final analysis, be treated likewise, although the constitution of these enzymes is still not perfectly known. Diastasic or enzymic actions are not always the work of one single ferment, but sometimes of two, each one activating the other. This has been the outcome of research by various physiologists, notably C. Delezenne (1868—1932). The important part played in these actions by certain simple bodies in infinitesimal quantities has also lately come to light: G. Bertrand demonstrated the presence of manganese in the case of laccase; Javillier and Delezenne found zinc in snake venom. We shall refer again to similar processes on the subject of vitamins and hormones. It is the organism's function to make these specific agents available directly or to localize them in certain organs; on these agents depend the transformations of substances (metabolism), which are among the most fundamental elements of physiological mechanisms.

Vitamins. Recently there has been a much publicized illustration of these special mechanisms in the study of nutrition. The whole of the energy exchanges, which constitute nutrition and which are termed digestion, excretion, respiration and thermic exchanges, take place basically through a series of oxidations and reductions. These processes liberate quantities of energy in the form of calories. Therefore it seemed to the chemists and physiologists of the late nineteenth century that the maintenance of the living machine simply entailed supplying the organism with the fuel to provide the necessary calories—2500 per day for the average man. This conception is still true in general terms, but recent progress in physiology has shown that the problem was much more complex, from the qualitative point of view. The experimental study of certain nutritional ailments, today known as deficiency diseases (beriberi, scurvy, pellagra, etc.), revealed that the cause of these ailments was to be found in the absence of certain essential substances in the diet. These need to be present only in the minutest quantities; they have been named *vitamins,* and in practice they are contained in our normal, everyday fresh foods. It has been possible to characterize on this basis a certain number of these under the letters A, B, C, D and E; the absence or insufficiency of each one of these determines one of the deficiency diseases. By means of particular diets, each of these diseases can be caused or cured at will. It is a simple matter of omitting a particular vitamin from the diets, or of re-introducing it. It now appears that a balance between the quantities of the various vitamins is necessary in a diet and, if this balance is broken, deficiency symptoms will appear. In quite recent years, the various vitamins have been isolated in a state of chemical purity (they are relatively simple compounds, ternary or nitrogenous) and they have been synthesized *in vitro*. In this very special and comparatively new aspect of nutritional problems, there is no mechanism that is specifically vital in the old sense of "vitalism." We have rather a series of physico-chemical mechanisms, depending on tiny amounts of determined substances and connected with the particular functioning of certain organs, like the liver or the suprarenal capsules. The organism is a very complicated laboratory with its own procedures for transforming substances or for contributing to the transformations; the vitamins act as catalysts in these procedures. The ideal diet cannot therefore be expressed, as once was thought, purely and simply by a certain number of calories; there are certain qualitative requirements in addition. The discovery of vitamins was an event of outstanding importance in physiology: its impact on present-day science can be compared to that made a century earlier by the discovery of enzymes.

Hormones and Endocrinology. There is a harmony in the functioning of the organism that suggests a multiplicity of final causes. But when the various phenomena are carefully analyzed, they can all be shown to depend on physico-chemical mechanisms. This fact was demonstrated yet again when present-day biology discovered a third category of substances that act, like enzymes and vitamins, in infinitesimal doses and govern the coordination of the organs and functions. These substances are *hormones.* The discovery and study of hormones only goes back to the early twentieth century. One of the most fruitful and important domains of present-day physiology, *endocrinology,* is devoted to these substances.

Physiologists had long recognized a whole series of special glandular organs, the thyroid (and the parathyroid) glands, the thymus, the pituitary gland, the suprarenal capsules. The function of these was not understood for a long time; structurally they are distinctive, first on account of their considerable vascularization, and second for the lack of any excretory outlet. Claude Bernard had called them internal-secretion glands (today we would say *endocrine* or *ductless* glands), as opposed to the ordinary or *exocrine* glands, which discharge their secretions through a duct, either directly outside or into the digestive tube. Bernard had wisely observed that the substances prepared in the endocrine glands must be passed into the blood stream or, in his own words, into the "milieu intérieur." He gave the first example of this when, in 1850, he discovered the glycogenic function of the liver. As it secretes bile, the liver is an exocrinal gland. But Bernard pointed out that it stores up, in its cells, the glucose brought by the cystic vein in the form of glycogen and that it restores this glycogen to the circulation, in the hepatic veins, as glucose. In this way it keeps the level of sugar in the blood constant. The liver does, therefore, have an internal or endocrine secretion.

Shortly afterward, some experiments by Brown-Séquard revealed the important role of the suprarenal capsules, removal of which is followed rapidly by death. Pathology had also shown how essential is the thyroid, and Pierre Marie later underlined the vital role of the pituitary gland. Other research work had pointed to the comparable importance of the pancreas; but all these data remained for a long time isolated and imprecise.

A misleading generalization on the notion of internal secretion had been formulated by Brown-Séquard: he extended it to every product of the disassimilation of tissues. Some of the experiments he carried out in 1889, upon himself, on glandular mechanisms were destined to arouse great public interest, and they paved the way for spectacular advances in endocrinology. At the age of seventy-two Brown-Séquard had himself injected with extracts from the testicles of young animals. As a result, he experienced renewed vigor and a rejuvenation that he explained by the action of substances which are produced in the testicles of young men but are absent in old age. These experiments were the subject of much publicity and controversy; they led to a new departure in therapeutics, namely the treatment of ailments due to a deficiency in an organ by the injection or ingestion of products extracted from the same organ in a healthy subject; this technique, known as opotherapy, led to some fruitful, as well as misleading, applications. It has also been the source of many works written since 1900 on internal-secretion glands.

The method employed was to study the ill-effects caused by the removal of these organs and to see to what extent they could be remedied by grafting on these same organs from another subject, or by administering extracts prepared in a variety of ways. Thus the principal function, or multiple functions, of the internal-secretion glands were elucidated. From each of these glands one or more substances have been characterized, then extracted chemically in a pure state and usually obtained directly by synthesis. These substances, which determine the specific action of the gland on the organism, are called *hormones*. For the thyroid, for example, the hormone is thyroxine, characterized by the presence of iodine; for the suprarenal capsules it is adrenalin (the outer zone of these organs secretes other hormones, only recently discovered, which act on the genital glands). Nothing at all was known about the function of the pituitary gland; today this gland is considered one of the most powerful of the organs, as it produces a whole series of hormones with multiple actions. Only the exocrine function of the pancreas was understood (secretion of pancreatic juice into the intestine). By the methods indicated above, an essential endocrine function was discovered in this organ (Hédon), namely the production of a special hormone, *insulin,* which originates in groups of cells known as the islands of Langerhans. Much of this new knowledge was due to Laguesse. A total lack or an insufficiency of insulin is the cause of acute diabetes, and the remedy is regular injections of this substance.

Other organs have now been shown to possess one or more important endocrine functions, alongside their exocrine role. The genital glands are a case in point. Today it is known that, in both sexes, these glands produce, in their parenchyma, a whole range of hormones, which have been analyzed chemically; these are sterols, and they derive from cholesterin, the formula of which is now known and which can be produced by synthesis. These sexual hormones control the differentiation of numerous secondary sexual characters, as well as the functioning of the genital apparatus. Their role is particularly interesting in mammalian females; these hormones govern the coordination of cyclic transformations, which insure that the embryo stays alive during its development in the uterus. The hormonal functioning of the genital glands is itself closely dependent on the pituitary gland, which is, so to speak, their life-giver, through the intermediary of other hormones that it produces (gonadotropic and prolans hormones). The story of this research is one of the most brilliant chapters in present-day histophysiology; the leading names are, for mammals, Bouin and Ancel; for birds, Pézard in France and Goodale in the United States. A host of other eminent research workers—embryologists, histologists, chemists and physiologists—have been inspired by this subject. Most of these hormones stimulate; there are, however, a few that inhibit, and these have been termed *chalones*.

Once again, space does not permit a detailed examination of all the facts, but an important idea underlying them is that hormones, produced by a particular organ and secreted into the blood stream, act, as it were, at a distance; they are in the nature of *chemical messengers,* which, by their reciprocal actions, harmonize and coordinate the functioning of the organs. It used to be thought that this effect was due exclusively to the nervous system. The discovery of hormones was, therefore, an entirely new and outstandingly important aspect of general physiology.

Indeed, the functioning of the nervous system itself seems also to be due to hormonal actions. Hormonal substances (especially acetylcholine for the parasympathetic) appear to control the linkage between the nervous cells (neurons), their articulations (synapses) and their terminations in the organs.

Finally, the role of the hormones also seems to be fundamental in the differentiation of the outlines and the organs within the embryo; the operation of the *organizer,* already mentioned in connection with Spemann, seems connected with this; furthermore, all doubt has recently been dispelled concerning the morphogenic action of the sexual hormones in the differentiation of the embryo's genital apparatus.

Like vitamins and enzymes, hormones act in infinitesimal doses and seem to constitute, at least in the higher organisms, a category of agents whose role is of primary importance. Further research may well reveal their presence in other, lower animals.

MICROBES AND THEIR ROLE IN NATURE;
PASTEUR

In the section on Lavoisier, reference was made to some of the ideas that his untimely death during the Revolution prevented him from formulating definitively. These ideas concerned the general cycle of living matter in nature, and we remarked that Pasteur was destined to complete them and draw the conclusions of Lavoisier's insight. The story of Pasteur's life and work is so well known that it need not be retold here; but, apart from his tremendous contributions to medicine, he produced a mass of data on some of the most fundamental aspects of life. His work must, therefore, be considered one of the great milestones in biology, and it is as such that we shall treat it here.

During his chemical researches into the hemihedral crystals of tartrate, Pasteur had seen that the transformations of substances effected by such lower organisms as fungi were closely connected with molecular dissymmetry, a fact he perceived as one of the characteristics of life. These notions have never been pursued very far from the biological point of view, although their value in chemistry has been enormous.

The work Pasteur did somewhat later at Lille on the subject of fermentations did, however, have immediate and far-reaching biological consequences. His studies of defective alcoholic fermentations enabled him to show that the cause of the deficiency was a parasitic fermentation, and this led him on to define and isolate, in a pure state, the lactic ferment. The whole chemistry of fermentations descends from the publication of these findings (a mere fifteen pages that appeared in 1857). The way was prepared for the specification of these fermentations, each of which is the result of nutritional exchanges in a determined organism and each of which produces definite chemical transformations in a given substance. Pasteur was soon to discover that certain fermentations only operate when protected from the air (anaerobic fermentations), for example, the butyric acid fermentation and putre-factions.

The fermentation that is brought about by brewer's yeast is due to the airless existence of this organism coming into contact with air and breathing in the ordinary way, thereby producing carbon dioxide. This work on fermentations transformed the various industries based upon them and provided, at the same time, a physiological explanation of the phenomenon itself. Previously, great chemists like Liebig and Berselius could find no better explanation than vitalist theories. Pasteur also provided the solution of the problem posed by Lavoisier about the cyclic return of organic substances to mineral matter.

Pasteur soon turned his attention to another great problem, that of *spontaneous generation,* which had been raised again, particularly as result of some experi-ments by A. Pouchet published in a book about *Heterogenesis* (1857). Pasteur proved by simple but crucial experiments that if a fermentescible or putre-fiable liquid is really protected against the germs in the air, it will remain sterile for an indefinite period. The so-called spontaneous generations were, in reality, the result of the germs in the atmosphere finding access to a liquid and multiplying therein without the observer realizing it. The whole bacteriological technique of sterilizing fermentescible media derived from this simple truth. Some years later, however, the controversy broke out again after some experiments by the Englishman Bastian (1876); this time Pasteur demonstrated that some germs, in the spore stage, can resist a temperature of 100° but not one of 120°. On this was based Chamberland's sterilizer, which is in use in every laboratory today. So, all alleged spontaneous generations were nothing more than the development of germs accidentally introduced into a medium that feeds them. We are able to see life continuing, but we may never witness it beginning.

Little need be said here about Pasteur's work on infectious diseases. His researches on the silkworm disease gradually led him into this domain. Like fermentations, infectious diseases originate in the contamination of the organism by specific germs. Pasteur devised well-known methods to attenuate the virulence of these diseases and to obtain vaccines that immunize against them.

The practical consequences of Pasteur's work are unequaled: it inaugurated a new era for medicine and surgery; it transformed, or created, a number of industries. Let us consider, by way of example, his notion of the part played by *germs* in the working of nature.

Infinitely tiny organisms, or *microbes,* as they have been called, the most widespread and important of which are the bacteria, were shown by Pasteur to play an enormous role in nature; they constitute tremendously powerful agents for chemical transformations, insofar as organic substances are concerned. This discovery is nothing less than a new general aspect of life and, as such, deserves pride of place as a milestone in biology.

Microbes are at work everywhere, especially in the earth, where they bring about important transformations of matter; some break down and others build up complex substances, like, for example, the nitrogenous compounds based on atmospheric nitrogen. Their function is, therefore, of primary importance in problems concerning the nutrition of plants through their roots. Plant physiology and agriculture were both transformed by Pasteur's doctrines and by the practical applications that were based on them by chemists and agronomists like Boussingault (1802—1887), Th. Schloesing (1829—1919) and his son A. T. Schloesing (1856—1930), Dehérain (1830—1902), Muntz (1846—1917), S. Winogradsky, etc. Great laboratories, like the one at Rothamsted in England, are still continuing the exploitation of this fruitful mine.

Among the major problems being studied is that of nutrition. The method used is synthetic, that is to say, all the substances and elements necessary to the development of an organism are determined individually. One of Pasteur's own students, Raulin (1836—

1896), solved this problem with admirable precision as it concerns a mold, *Aspergillus niger*. More recently A. Maze applied the same method to a higher plant, maize. Nowadays much research is devoted to the individual species of Protozoa and the thallophytes in order to determine which syntheses each is capable of effecting and which ones it cannot accomplish, unless provided with certain ready-made compounds known as *growth factors*.

Each successful piece of research reveals physico-chemical mechanisms to explain phenomena that were previously considered to belong to the mysterious domain of life. Pasteur found himself in conflict with Claude Bernard after the latter's death (1878). The production of alcohol by yeast during alcoholic fermentation seems to result directly from the *life* of the yeast. Pasteur did not draw a vitalist conclusion from this, but had not been able to find any intermediary agent between the living substance and the transformed sugar-substances. Shortly before his death, Bernard had conducted experiments to try to reduce these transformations to purely mechanical physico-chemical processes. He left some notes, which were published and which decided Pasteur to conduct some fresh experiments; in these, the latter proved that the facts discovered by Bernard and considered *provisionally* by him to be direct and purely chemical transformations of grape juice were, in fact, due to the intervention of yeasts. When the unripe grapes were protected against the germs in the air and, above all, against the yeast that under normal conditions is always present on the surface of the grapes, the fermentation obtained by Bernard did not, in fact, take place.

But the essence of the problem considered by Bernard was eventually solved a few years later (1897) in a manner that contradicted neither his views nor the facts analyzed by Pasteur. By *crushing* yeast cells, Büchner was able to extract from the pulp, which is no longer alive, a ferment, zymase, which is the real agent of the transformation of sugar into alcohol and which normally remains inside the living cell; therefore, under normal conditions, fermentation appears to be a vital operation of the cell, but its real agent is a soluble ferment of the same order as those that effect all transformations of matter; as in digestion, for example. This is an outstanding example of progress in the study of those vital phenomena that, one by one, are being categorized as physico-chemical mechanisms.

The Science of Heredity: Genetics

The various biological disciplines considered so far, whether morphological or physiological, are concerned with the individual. Another branch of science came into being with the twentieth century; it deals with consolidated observations extending over successive generations; it envisages the problems of heredity and of *genetics*.

Since time immemorial men have been impressed by manifestations of heredity. The variable degree of similarity in successive generations of families, the creation of breeds of domestic animals and varieties of plants according to the whim of animal-breeders or agriculturists, above all the striking transmission of certain anomalies—these phenomena are a matter of everyday observation; speculation and ideas about them were current long before science existed. These ideas were, however, mostly concerned with the oddities of heredity, and it is only during the last few decades that some of the secrets of this new discipline have been revealed. Today the study of heredity stands as an ordered science in which rational forecasting and calculation are possible.

On account of their complexity, biological processes can almost always be analyzed, not in their normal functioning, but in their anomalies. In matters of heredity, an abnormal case is one of a cross between distinct races, varieties or even species. Some such crosses have been in current practice for a long time; it is many centuries since man first crossed horse and donkey to obtain male or female mules, which are, of course, invariably sterile. Crosses between races or species of poultry, pheasants, ducks, goldfinch and canary, etc., are also by no means novel. All these results have been obtained in a very empirical manner.

In the early eighteenth century the way was opened that was to lead, nearly 200 years later, to genetics. At that early date, the true nature of stamens as the male organs of the plant was already appreciated. Cesalpino had put his faith in Aristotelian doctrines and denied any sexuality in plants; Tournefort still regarded the stamens as organs of excretion. Theophrastus had intuitive foresight into the real role of the stamens concerning the fertilization and productivity of the date palm and the caprification of fig trees. Camerarius finally affirmed their nature as male organs in his *Epistola de sexu plantarum*, published in 1691 at Tübingen. In 1751 a new method was inaugurated by Koelreuter, who used the pollen of one species to fertilize another. In this way he crossed two tobacco plants (*Nicotiana rustica* and *N. paniculata*), obtaining hybrids and about a score of successive generations by fertilizing these hybrids with the pollen of one or the other of the parents; this meant that these generations made a progressive return to the species of one of the parent plants. This kind of research was further developed by the Dutchman Gärtner, who published voluminous works about hybridization (1844). In France, Sageret made a judicious choice of subjects when he crossed two varieties of melon, the chaté (*m*) and the cantaloupe (*c*).

The resulting hybrid melons showed, alongside one another, some characters of each parent variety; for example, yellow flesh (*m*) with white seeds (*c*); a speckled appearance (*c*), size of segments intermediary between *m* and *c*, an acid taste (*c*); in other hybrids, the characters of the two parent types would be shared out differently. These *disjuncted* characters were something new, and Sageret must be considered an important precursor.

The year 1865 was marked by the independent and simultaneous publication of two remarkable works. In Paris, Naudin (1815—1899) published a thesis that won the special prize for physical sciences offered by the Académie des Sciences. It was an account of hybridization experiments conducted on many species, and its influence is still considerable. The second work contained the results obtained by Mendel (1822—1884), an Augustan monk from Brünn in Moravia. He had made methodical crossings between varieties of peas *(Pisum sativum)* that differed from one another in one or more respects (such as flower color, smooth or wrinkled seeds, small or large size, etc.). Naudin and Mendel arrived at almost identical conclusions although neither knew anything of the work of the other. Mendel's findings made a greater impact, as he expressed them more categorically and gave them a statistical and mathematical form.

They can be summarized in a few lines if we use the simplest example studied by Mendel—the cross between peas with smooth seeds (S) and those with wrinkled seeds (W). At the first generation, F_1, we obtain 100 per cent of smooth seeds, and, at the second, F_2 (as a result of the self-fertilization of the F_1 plants) we obtain 75 per cent of S seeds and 25 per cent of W. The W character reappears therefore in F_1, in spite of appearances to the contrary. In the F_1 hybrid, W was only *masked* or *hidden* by the S character, which is termed *dominant*. In F_2 there is a disjunction, wich causes W to reappear. This latter character is termed *recessive.* The explanation is that *the hybrid F₁ has a mixed SW constitution, but its reproductive cells (gametes) are pure, S or W,* the two categories being of equal frequency. In fertilizations leading to the F_2 seeds, the combinations of S and W gametes are made haphazardly and consequently, by law of probabilities, should give: 1 SS; 2 SW; 3 WW; by reason of the dominance of S, the SW seeds are smooth, and we should expect $3S : 1W$. This is in fact what happens. If the different F_2 seeds are cultivated seperately, it transpires that one-third of the smooth seeds are reproduced in a pure state (these are the SS); the remaining two-thirds, however, once again produce three-fourths of S seeds and one-fourth of W; finally, the wrinkled seeds are reproduced in a pure state W.

Mendel also made crosses between varieties of peas that differed from one another, not by one, but by several characters. He discovered that the same laws still applied, each pair of differential characters behaving just as if they were a single one. In this way, it was possible to foretell precisely how the various generations would be constituted. Thus pure chance, which had hitherto seemed to be the essential characteristic of heredity, was supplanted by perfectly foreseeable regularity.

It is astonishing that such decisive and clearly formulated results should have aroused no interest.[10] Moreover, Naudin's findings fully supported Mendel,

[10]Although Darwin discusses Naudin's works in his *Variations of Animals and Plants under Domestication* (London, 1868).

even if they lacked the same numerical precision. The efforts of both men were literally ignored for thirty-five years. It was not until 1900 that three botanists, working simultaneously but independently, drew attention to these experiments and confirmed them by various examples; they were H. de Vries in Holland, C. Correns in Germany, and E. von Tschermak in Austria. This time the impact was immediate and resounding; an enormous experimental movement was unleashed and, within a few years, Mendel's laws had been verified on a great variety of plants and animals. Genetics, the science of heredity, came into being; its instigators were the three authors just mentioned and W. Bateson in England, L. Cuénot in France, W. Castle and, soon afterward, T. Morgan in the United States, as well as many others.

Not all the cases are as simple as the fundamental type summarized above, but there is obviously not room here to give a detailed account of the various categories that have been revealed and that constitute the present-day content of genetics. Mention should be made, however, of the magnificent research of T. Morgan and his collaborators, C. Bridges, H. Müller and A. Sturtevant, on the fruit fly, *Drosophila melanogaster*. These flies have proved eminently suitable material for this work, on account of the ease of breeding them, their rapidity of reproduction, and the great number of individuals produced. While breeding these flies, Morgan was aware of a large number of sudden variations (these mutations will be mentioned again later), which are hereditary and conform to Mendel's laws. The combination of all these mutations among themselves have provided material of enormous scope and of primary importance for the study of heredity. *Drosophila* has spread from Morgan's workbench into laboratories all over the world, and the conclusions obtained from this species have been extended to a great variety of plants and animals.

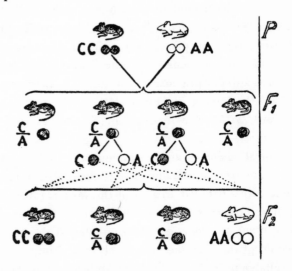

Fig. 11. Mendelian heredity. Gray mouse crossed with white mouse. (Cuénot, *Genèse des Espèces.*)

Moreover, his work on *Drosophila* enabled Morgan to reconcile Mendel's laws to the fundamental facts of cytology, as they concern the chromosomes of the nucleus, and to construct the *chromosomic theory of heredity*. The hereditary transmission of 400 mutations was followed through; those 400 were divided into four numerically unequal groups. All the hereditary factors were grouped into these four linkage-systems, one for each pair of chromosomes.

On the other hand, the *Drosophila* nuclei can be seen to have *four* pairs of chromosomes. The facts that emerged from many experiments led Morgan to realize that the various mutations obtained and contrived by himself are determined by localized alterations in the chromosomes of the nucleus, each change corresponding to one definite unit or *gene*. He was able to locate these genes, *in the various chromosomes, at precise points*. The results of the experiences and the theory thus established are in complete concordance. Everything that cytology teaches us about the constitution of the reproductive cells and about fertilization makes a perfect setting for the findings of genetics. The chromosomes of the nucleus, with their genes localized on them, are basically the vehicle of hereditary properties.

It is significant to compare the enormous success of the conceptions of Naudin and Mendel in 1900 with the general indifference that greeted their publications in 1865. The contrast can largely be explained by the fact that, in the interval, all the data necessary for an adequate representation of their theories had been acquired. This information related to cellular division, to the formation of gametes, and to fertilization. Thus it can be seen that, in the sciences generally and in biology particularly, much depends on the circumstances and timing of publication.

Since 1900 the science of genetics has developed considerably in scope and coherence. This does not mean that all the problems of heredity have been solved once and for all. In spite of their extensive application, Mendel's laws represent only the simplest form of hereditary transmission, and we are still faced with much more complex cases. Genetics has therefore emerged from the mere experimental study of crosses between races or varieties. Crosses between species, when they are fertile, are considerably more complicated. Some have been successfully and penetratingly analyzed in certain plants, especially by E. Baur working on the species *Antirrhinum*. In animals, crossings between species are almost invariably sterile, but Mlle. G. Cousin has discovered a case (between two species of cricket, *Gryllus campestris* and *Gr. bimaculatus*) where the offspring are fertile. The analysis of these results promises to be very enlightening.

Finally, there exists today a flourishing science of heredity the founding of which constitutes an important milestone in twentieth-century biology.

Evolution

The preceding sections reveal the gradual development of an understanding of the phenomenon of life. This had already found an important expression during the nineteenth century with the theory of evolution.

The origins of this theory go back to the eighteenth century, when the notion of species was established. The orthodox tradition of species stems from Genesis. "There are as many species," said Linnaeus, "as the Infinite Being created in the beginning." But even then, the idea of the progressive formation of species was making its appearance. Buffon, whose influence over his contemporaries was considerable, envisaged natural history in a philosophical manner. He believed intuitively in a long history of the earth and of geological phenomena, boldly estimating the age of the earth as 60,000 years, instead of the traditional 6,000 (today we count in billions of years). In his *Discours sur la dégénération des animaux*,[11] he declared that the 200 species whose story he had described "may be reduced to a certain number of families or main groups, *from which it is not impossible that all the others may have descended*." He pointed out the parallelism between the quadrupeds of the Old and the New Worlds and attributed the differences between both stocks to the action of climate and other circumstances; likewise he considered that domestic animals must have undergone changes as a result of man's interference. Similar ideas can be found in the works of Condillac.

LAMARCK AND THE ADAPTATION OF
ORGANISMS

Lamarck was a personal friend of Buffon's, and much influenced by his thought. He nevertheless is un-

[11]*Histoire naturelle*, Vol. XIV.

deniably the founder of transformist doctrines, which he propounded in his museum lectures and then published in his *Philosophie Zoologique* (1809). He contested the absolute value of the species, insisting that the individual is the only real unit. The individual is subjected to the influence of the conditions in which it lives; its needs determine its habits and consequently it makes repeated use of certain organs and less use of others. Thus as a result of usage or non-usage, we have cases of hypertrophy or atrophy, and *these acquired modifications are transmitted by heredity*. In this way, types become gradually modified, in harmony with surrounding conditions, or with what Comte called the *milieu*. This is the origin of the adaptive character of the structure of organisms, which is a *result*, and not the a priori expression of creative thought. This doctrine is complete and coherent. According to Lamarck, nature only needs time and favorable circumstances to operate any transformation. Nature was always producing simple beings that gradually evolved into other, more complex ones. Applying the same ideas to the mineral world, Lamarck opposed Cuvier's notion of catastrophes and formulated what was to become in geology, with Lyell, the theory of actualistic causes. This, basically, was Lamarck's novel and revolutionary conception. It ran up against the positivist and traditionalist mind of Cuvier, who fought against it and discredited it in the eyes of their contemporaries. It must be admitted that Lamarck's theories had, at that time, no solid basis of fact on which to stand and were propped up on arguments that were often weak, even puerile, or that invoked outmoded notions, like spontaneous generation. Even today, the heredity of acquired modifications, the cornerstone of Lamarckian doctrine, remains a hypothesis that conflicts with experience. E. Geoffroy Saint-Hilaire was more cautiously moving toward evolutionist conceptions on the anatomical plane; but he tended to exaggerate the idea of a unified plan of composition extending to the whole animal kingdom. Against this, he had sound insight into the usefulness of embryogeny for determining the affinities of organisms. He also foresaw the essential value of rudimentary organs as vestiges of previous states, and among the striking examples he gave of this we could mention the traces of teeth that are discernible in whale fetuses. Finally, he had perceived that freaks are accidental deviations from normal anatomy that may eventually lead to new forms. Therefore, Geoffroy Saint-Hilaire deserves to rank among the founders of transformist doctrines.

DARWIN AND NATURAL SELECTION

Due mainly to the opposition of Cuvier, these doctrines underwent a total eclipse until they reappeared triumphantly in 1859, based on entirely new material, with the *Origin of Species,* by Charles Darwin (1809—1882). Darwin's conceptions spring from observations he made during his journey around the world in the *Beagle* (1831—1836), and especially in South America and the Galapagos Islands. The detailed comparisons of a same type particularly in the various islands of this archipelago had suggested to him the idea of the general variability of species. While living in the countryside at Down after his return to England, he devoted himself, from 1842 on, to the study of this variability. In 1838 he read the *Essay on the Principle of Population* by the clergyman Thomas Malthus (1798), and this book gave him the idea of the importance of *vital competition between individuals* and between species leading consequently to the *survival of the fittest*. This is equivalent to nature's making an automatic choice of the individuals best adapted to the conditions of their existence—in other words, *natural selection*. Darwin was a conscientious and thorough observer with a liking for indisputable facts. He found plenty of these, in England, in the highly developed methods employed in stockbreeding and agriculture; man *chooses* the reproducers or the seeds with a view to perpetuating and developing particularities that have already been accomplished and that are considered desirable. This is conscious, *artificial selection,* which Darwin saw as a reflection of natural selection. Competition and selection became, in Darwin's thinking, the fundamental factors in variation and in the gradual transformation of natural species. Unlike Lamarck, Darwin did not concern himself with the causes of the variations; he simply accepted them as a matter of observation and only speculated about their ultimate fate. He had already collected an enormous amount of material on the subject of natural selection when, in 1858, the same ideas were formulated in a letter written to the geologist Lyell by A. R. Wallace (1823—1913), who was at the time involved in a zoological exploration of Malaya. At Lyell's suggestion, the two papers by Darwin and Wallace were read to a meeting of the Linnaean Society in London in July, 1858. The following year, Darwin published a book containing the essence of his ideas. This was his famous *Origin of Species*. A few years later, the mass of material collected by Darwin appeared in two volumes on the *Variations of Animals and Plants under Domestication* (1868).

The *Origin of Species* made a colossal impact and unleashed many furious and lengthy arguments. However, this time the cause of transformism was won, and the idea of evolution was to dominate all biological thinking by the end of the nineteenth century. A little book, *Für Darwin,* was published in 1865 by an eminent German zoologist living in Brazil, Fritz Müller. In it he transposed the Darwinian doctrine into embryogeny; the great variety of larval forms, through which many marine animals pass (especially shrimps of the Penaeidae family), were considered by Müller to represent, in a transitory fashion, forms through which the species had previously passed. He interpreted the development of the individual *(ontogeny)* as an *abbreviated recapitulation* of the previous history of the species *(phylogeny)*. A conception of this nature had already been formed, on a purely conceptual plane, in Germany by Meckel, and in France by Serres, a disciple of Geoffroy Saint-Hilaire. E. Haeckel based his *fundamental biogenetic law* on the idea developed by Müller. He expanded this theme in a series of books that found a very wide reading public. He was the great publicist of the theory of evolution, and it was he who oriented this theory toward embryogeny, which thus became the most fruitful field of zoological research in the last decades of the nineteenth century. The enormous progress made in this research was due to transformist conceptions. Today it appears, however, that the fundamental biogenetic law has been misapplied. Even if vestiges of former states can be found in the embryo, embryology is essentially a *present* process, not a retrospective one. Such vestiges as are preserved do not correspond to any recapitulatory principle but are rather those of organs that are still effective and functional. The function may sometimes be a new one, or it may have served in the building of new organs. Nevertheless the reaction against the ideas of Müller and Haeckel and against the very idea of evolution was excessive and ill-founded. Indeed, not only embryogeny, but also comparative anatomy, animal and plant paleontology, and the general study of floras and faunas have all contributed to the general authority of the transformist conceptions; today these are regarded as the only possible, rational explanation for nature, past and present.

Darwin did not reject Lamarck's ideas out of hand; he even admitted the heredity of acquired modifications as proven. Haeckel rehabilitated all the work of

Lamarck, whose theories found many eminent protagonists, like A. Giard, E. Perrier, G. Bonnier, F. le Dantec
in France, Eimer, L. Plate in Germany, etc.

WEISMANN AND SOMATO-GERMINAL DUALISM

About 1890 A. Weismann reviewed the general
position of the problem and formulated a completely
new theory of heredity. He refused to accept the fact
or even the possibility that acquired modifications are
handed down to posterity by the individual. Wallace
adopted the same standpoint concerning the inheritance of acquired characters and, like Weismann,
questioned the validity of Lamarckian theories. In
Weismann's new theory, the reproductive cells (germen)
are quite distinct from the rest of the organism (soma).
The germen alone is of any importance to the species,
the soma being nothing more than a perishable covering, belonging solely to the individual. Weismann
could not see how a modification localized in the soma
could possibly be inscribed as such in the germen.
These ideas, which rested on recently acquired knowledge and were developed with great ingenuity and
logic, have proved very influential in the last fifty years.
It must be admitted that the criticism of the facts
quoted in favor of the heredity of acquired characters
is very much to the point; indeed, many experiments
have been attempted in order to establish the reality of
the transmission of acquired modifications. Up to the
present, they have all been in vain.

HUGO DE VRIES AND MUTATIONISM

A new chapter in the story of transformism was opened in 1900, by H. de Vries' theory of *mutations*. De Vries also considers that the variations provoked by the action of the "milieu" are purely individual and the species itself remains stable. At times, however, something in the nature of an explosion occurs and produces groups of sudden hereditary variations. These are *mutations,* and they give rise to new elementary species. Jordan, the French botanist, formulated conceptions that closely agreed with this idea. De Vries based his theory on known facts; many stable varieties had in fact appeared suddenly during historical time. A Russian botanist, Korschinski, had already collected a quantity of such factual evidence, which he qualified with the term *heterogenesis.* But De Vries thought he had discovered an example of these multiple, discontinuous and hereditary variations in a plant of the onagraceae family, *Oenothera lamarckiana.* He devoted more than twenty years of experimental research to this species, and the results are of great value and interest. The conception of heredity that De Vries formulated following his study of this plant has now been abandoned. The facts that emerged concerning *Oenothera lamarckiana*, and that apply to some extent to other plants of the genus, have been the object of much careful analysis. It is now known that the "mutations" are in fact hybridization processes. De Vries's work still constitutes an important chapter in genetics, even if it cannot be regarded as part of the foundation of a general theory of evolution.

THE PRESENT STATE OF THE PROBLEM

It is apparent from what has been written above that the fact of evolution is now firmly established, whereas much remains to be elucidated concerning the way in which it has been taking place. The predominant tendency at the present time, especially in England, rests on the Darwinian idea of selection, applied to sudden variations or mutations (but not including those in the genus *Oenothera*). Lamarckism is rather out of favor, and yet adaptation is an irrefutable fact of very wide application. It is not being claimed that all the particularities of organisms have an adaptive character; but it is, to say the least, questionable that adaptation is accomplished by mere chance.

Not only does a precise and harmonious correlation between functions and structures exist in every organism, but most species also have numerous peculiarities that correspond closely to the conditions of the animal's life. Moreover, there are many striking examples of special pieces of apparatus, the parts of which are arranged to fit together like tools invented by man. Cuénot has termed these arrangements *coaptations*.[12]

Every part is completely formed during the individual's development, long before any use is made of it. Fig. 12 shows us a curious example of this in the

[12]L. Cuénot, *L'Adaptation* (Paris, 1929), pp. 265 *et seq*.

Larva of the Passalidae.[13] The third foot on each side
p_3 is reduced to a stump, and it ends in claws that
scrape against a striated part of the base (coxa) of the
second foot p_2; this striation is situated at just the
right level to form a stridulating organ, rather reminis-
cent of a guitar. This is obviously an adaptive arrangement, which must result from an evolution (the same
device is found in less complete form in closely related
families). How was this adaptation accomplished? We
do not know, but it is not easy to see nothing more in
this than the mere result of a series of hazards in the
variations of the species.

[13]The *Passalidae* are a family of large lamellicorn beetles
(about 500 species, distributed mainly in the tropics) that dig
galleries under the bark of dead trees. Their behavior has been
studied by F. Ohaus (*Stettin. Entom. Zeit.*, LX, 1899; LXI, 1900;
LXX, 1909) and by W. M. Wheeler (*Trans. Amer. Phil. Soc.*,
XXII, 1920, pp. 274-275; *Scientific Monthly*, XIV, 1922, pp.
513-514). They are said to live in familes, both parents and
offspring together. Their stridulation is so loud that it reveals
their position behind the bark and apparently serves to rally
together the individuals belonging to the same group. However,
R. Heymons (*Zeits. f. Morph. Oekol.*, XVI, 1930), who more
recently has made precise observations and experiments on these
animals in Brazil, *refutes* the *social* character of the life of these
insects. He claims that stridulation is merely an instinctive
reaction to any unexpected disturbance, both on the part of
larvae and of adults.

The adult's stridulating apparatus is quite unlike the
larva's. It works by the rubbing together of little teethlike
protuberances situated respectively on the dorsal surface of
the abdomen and on the lower surface of the wings. This is an
example of a twofold differentiation within the same species;
larva and adult possess the same adaptation by means of completely dissimilar anatomical arrangements.

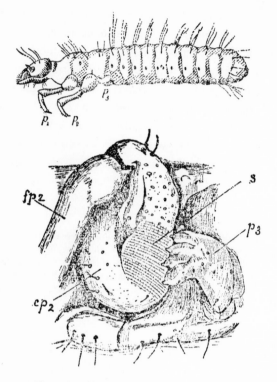

Fig. 12. *Above,* young larva (first stage) of *Passalus* (after R. Heymons); *below,* view of part of the side of the mesothorax and metathorax of a passalid larva from Borneo. cp_2, fp_2, coxa and base of the femur of the second leg (p_2); S, striated surface forming a stridulation organ; p_3, very short third leg with claws, scratching the surface S. (After David Sharp.)

Many decisive and factual arguments are supplied by paleontology in support of the idea of evolution. But the paleontological evidence is only fragmentary, and, as has been said above, it does not reveal the real origin of the various groups or offer us access to the origins of life on earth.[14] All these fundamental problems are still largely a matter of conjecture. However, it can safely be said that evolution is a process which covers the whole history of the earth, but it does not repeat itself and it is irreversible. By its very nature, it is a problem not very well suited to the experimental method. It must be admitted, therefore, that this is a subject on which there is still a great deal to be learned.

[14]A. Dauvillier has formulated some very interesting considerations, based on chemistry, about the origins of life. He postulates that life could have found conditions for creation by synthesis at a determined period in time and that these same conditions have not been produced since that time (A. Dauvillier and E. Desguin, *Sur l'origine de la Vie* [*Revue Scientifique,* 1940], pp. 292-296).

EPILOGUE

So we come to the end of this brief review; in it we
have tried to throw some light on the manifold aspects
and successive stages that mark the progress of biological knowledge from antiquity to the present day. The
vicissitudes in the story would seem to spring both from
contingent circumstances and from conditions that are
simply in the nature of things.

The contingent circumstances depend on the
historical background. The collapse of Greco-Roman
civilization resulted in a great gap in the advance of
knowledge. The hiatus corresponds to the Middle
Ages, which clearly separate the ancient from the
modern in science. When ancient science was exhumed
in the Renaissance it was, to some extent, equivalent
to a brake on progress, or to a curtain that concealed
reality from view and delayed man's analysis of nature.

The "conditions that are simply in the nature of

things" are due to the very complexity of living processes. The superior minds who tackled these problems were naturally induced to allow speculation to fill the gaps in their knowledge. One of the essential aspects of the advance of biological science was the gradual retreat and disappearance of such phantoms as animism, vitalism and finality. One by one they were replaced by more and more precise physico-chemical interpretations of life's various manifestations. But final victory depended, of course, on the complete emancipation of chemistry and physics, and it is therefore no coincidence that the nineteenth century witnessed the triumphant rise of biology. Everything that preceded this period could be nothing more than preparatory. Description and passive observation allowed little more than provisional glimpses of the secrets of nature, and only a few outstanding men (like Harvey, Réaumur, Spallanzani, Lavoisier) realized the vital role of experimentation and paved the way for the nineteenth-century triumphs of Bernard and Pasteur.

It is significant that the term *biology* was coined in 1802, on the very threshold of the century. One of the main features of the nineteenth century was, in fact, the unification of the sciences of life. This unity was achieved through knowledge of the *cell* as the common basis of the organization and functioning of all organisms, from the lowest to the highest, at every stage of their existence from the unicellular egg up to the extreme complexity of the organisms that make up the adult individual. All biological problems were reduced to the cellular scale and to the study of the appropriate mechanisms, which are brought into play by the cell, in its exchanges with the surrounding world. The preceding pages give some idea of the progress achieved in this study of the gradual convergence of acquired knowledge. Although we have traveled a long way, there are still many unmapped paths before us.

If, in fact, each of the elementary processes of life can be more or less completely explained on a physico-chemical basis, that still hardly helps us to comprehend how the coordination and the harmony of the whole machine is accomplished. How do the processes follow one another; how do they lead from the initial cell or egg to the adult organism, which is so strictly defined and yet so amazingly heterogeneous? What of the perfect adjustment and the synergetic functioning of the various parts of the organism? It is difficult to answer without resorting to some kind of "finality" explanation, whereby living matter is somehow distinct from the rest of nature.

If we look backward into time, we meet an equally baffling enigma. We have seen how much obscurity surrounds the problem of evolution and how ignorant we are of the origin of life. At some infinitely distant period in the past, life seems to have begun in conditions that have apparently never been reproduced since and about which we still know nothing. We can observe life that has been continuing ever since that period, but we cannot see life beginning anew. This explains why the essential modalities of life are still enveloped in mystery for us. The efforts of each new scientific generation dispel a certain amount of darkness, but they do not prevent that darkness from persisting before our eyes in new forms.

The most recent milestone in biology may, therefore, be summarized as the successful reduction of the elementary vital processes to purely physico-chemical mechanisms. This represents a major scientific conquest, and its application is general and definitive. Among the milestones that may be reached in the future are the penetration of the secret of life itself and the answer to the question—Can life be fully reduced to a mechanical concept of the same order?

The radical solution to this riddle would consist in the successful creation out of lifeless components of substances having all the properties of living matter. Thus would be accomplished that phenomenon of spontaneous generation that has always turned out to be a disappointing illusion. Perhaps it will never be anything else, if life is really not reducible to the properties of non-living substances, however complex these may be.

In recent times, physics and chemistry have made the alchemist's dream come true: by means of radiations, elements can now be transmuted in the laboratory. These same sciences also reveal that determinism, in the strict, classical sense, does not have an absolute application and ceases to exist in the domain and on the scale of atoms. In this sphere we find only uncertainties and probabilities, on the basis of quanta. Might there not be a similar or reverse scale applicable to the immensity of space and time, embracing the infinity of the past? The laws governing the present-day world would no longer rigorously apply on this scale; above all they would not be applicable to the initial conditions that allowed life to begin on earth, with all its special modalities. And might there not be, in our world today, special resultants, whose existence we do not yet suspect, for the physico-chemical functioning of living substance? How recent, for example, is our knowledge of the dimensions and complexity of molecules! These still unknown resultants could be at the basis of the peculiarities of the constitution of organisms and of evolution. These phenomena baffle us simply because they are not reducible to our laws governing the inorganic world.[1]

There is a question mark on each milestone in biology which stretches ahead of us into the future.

[1]Quantum physicists have already considered what bearing the quanta theory may have on general problems of biology. My colleague and friend Louis de Broglie has pointed out to me a book by P. Jordan, *Anschauliche Quantentheorie* (Berlin, 1936), in which a whole chapter is devoted to this question ("Kausalität und Statistik im Organischen," pp. 292-302). The following is a brief summary of it.

N. Bohr had already suggested that atomic and quantum physics should afford us a more intimate understanding of biological phenomena, whereas a *complete* reduction of biological laws to classical physics would, in all probability, not be possible.

Jordan considers that the elementary processes of life and its fundamental reactions take place on the atomic scale and depend on the action of catalysts, *organizers*, etc. Life is essentially an ensemble of micro-physical processes. On the other hand, the processes of heredity present a discontinuous aspect, which is comparable to that of quanta, and they constitute the most convincing and the broadest possible basis for a concept of this order. These basic discontinuities introduce the need for *statistical* considerations in fundamental biological processes. Consequently, when cases are considered in isolation, we can no longer speak of strict determinism but only of likelihoods. These are in proportion to the intensity of the acting forces and of other factors.

Jordan is thus able to conceive a priori the possibility of inheriting acquired characters through the repercussion of somatic phenotypic modifications on the germinal cells; it is most difficult to produce positive cases of this type experimentally because they are *statistically* very rare. This would offer a plausible explanation of the failure of attempts to prove by experiment that acquired characters can be inherited.

Furthermore, if the general behavior of an organism can only be defined statistically, then only the *average* behavior of a population is determinable; this throws new light on the problem of freedom. Liberty amounts, in effect, to the possibility of choosing the most appropriate way of reacting from a variety of possible ways. The absence of strict causality in quantum physics makes it feasible for the organism to have a choice between resultant reactions, and, consequently, finality is not ruled out.

SELECTED BIBLIOGRAPHY

Beck, William S. *Modern Science and the Nature of Life*. New York: Doubleday & Co. (Paperback.)

Bernal, J. D. "The Origin of Life," *New Biology*, Vol. XVI (1954).

Bernard, Claude. *La science expérimentale*. Paris, 1855.

Buffon, George, Comte de. *Oeuvres complètes*. Paris, 1778.

Castiglioni, Arturo. *A History of Medicine*. New York: Alfred A. Knopf, 1947.

Cesalpino, Andreas. *De Plantis*. Rome, 1603.

Cuénot, L. *L'influence du milieu sur les animaux*. Paris, 1894.

Cuvier, Georges. *Le règne animal*. Paris, 1817.

——. *Leçons d'anatomie comparée*. Paris, 1799.

——. *Recherches sur les ossements fossilés de quadrupèdes*. Paris, 1812.

Darwin, Charles. *The Origin of Species* and *The Descent of Man*. New York: Modern Library.

De Kruif, Paul. *Microbe Hunters*. New York: Harcourt, Brace & Co., 1932.

Descartes, René. *Philosophical Works,* tr. E. S. Haldane and G. R. T. Ross. New York: Dover Publications, 1955. (Paperback.)

Driesch, Hans. *History and Theory of Vitalism.* New York: The Macmillan Co., 1914.

Dubos, René J. *Louis Pasteur, Free Lance of Science.* Boston: Little, Brown and Co., 1950.

Glass, B. "The Long Neglect of a Scientific Discovery: Mendel's Laws of Inheritance." In George Boas and others, *Studies in Intellectual History.* Baltimore: Johns Hopkins Press, 1953.

Goldschmidt, Richard B. *Understanding Heredity.* New York: John Wiley & Sons, 1952.

Grew, Nehemiah. *The Anatomy of Vegetables.* London, 1672.

Harvey, William. *Motion of the Heart and Blood.* New York: E. P. Dutton & Co. (Paperback.)

Hooke, Robert. *Micrographia.* New York: Dover Publications. (Paperback.)

Huxley, Julian. *Evolution: The Modern Synthesis.* New York: Harper & Brothers, 1942.

Jussieu, A. L. de. *Genera Plantarum.* Paris, 1789.

Lamarck, Jean Baptiste de. *Histoire naturelle des animaux sans vertèbres.* Paris, 1815.

Lavoisier, Antoine L. *Oeuvres.* Paris, 1863.

Leeuwenhoek, Antony van. *Opera omnia.* Leyden, 1722.

Linnaeus, Carolus. *Systema naturae.* Leyden, 1735.

Luria, Salvador E. *General Virology.* New York: John Wiley & Sons, 1953.

Lyell, Charles. *Elements of Geology.* London, 1832.

Malpighi, Marcello. *Opera omnia.* Leyden, 1687.

Montagu, M. "Vesalius and the Galenists," *Scientific Monthly,* Vol. LXXX (1955).

Morgan, Thomas Hunt. *The Mechanism of Mendelian Heredity.* New York, 1915.

Nelsen, O. *Comparative Embryology of Vertebrates.* New York: Blakiston Co., 1953.

Pagel, Walter. "The Reaction to Aristotle in Seventeenth-Century Biological Thought." In E. Underwood (ed.), *Science, Medicine and History.* New York: Oxford University Press, 1953.

Pasteur, Louis. *Etudes sur le vin.* Paris, 1866.
——. *Etudes sur le vinaigre.* Paris, 1866.

Réaumur, René de. *Mémoire pour servir à l'histoire des insectes.* Paris, 1734.

Russell, F. S., and C. M. Yonge. *The Seas: Our Knowledge of Life in the Sea, And How It Is Gained.* New York: Frederick Warne & Co.

Sarton, George. *Galen of Pergamon.* Lawrence, Kansas: University of Kansas Press, 1954.

Shrock, R. R., and William Twenhofel. *Principles of Invertebrate Paleontology.* New York: McGraw-Hill Book Co., 1953.

Simpson, George G. *The Major Features of Evolution.* New York: Columbia University Press, 1953.

Swammerdam, Jan. *Bibel der Natur.* Leipzig, 1752.

Vesalius, Andreas. *De humani corporis fabrica.* Basel, 1543.

Woodruff, L. "Microscopy before the 19th Century," *Biological Symposia,* Vol. I (1940).

INDEX